How to Dump a Body at Sea and Not Get Caught

The Al Ferrari Story

SPEAKING VOLUMES, LLC
NAPLES, FLORIDA
2024

How to Dump a Body at Sea and Not Get Caught— The Al Ferrari Story

Cover artwork by Steven Strumpf

ISBN 979-8-89022-034-9

HOW TO DUMP A BODY AT SEA AND NOT GET CAUGHT

THE AL FERRARI STORY

Mack Maloney & Marc Zappulla

A True Crime Novel

Mack Maloney:
For my cousin, Eileen

Marc Zappulla:
For my parents, whose strength and
resolve inspire me every day.

Introduction

This book is a compilation of interviews, transcripts, notes, and personal recollections pertaining to the life of Al Ferrari, once named "The Year's Most Interesting Citizen" in Everett, Massachusetts. All the crimes described are true. Some names have been changed to protect the identities of living persons. Thanks to the *Boston Herald-American* for use of their reporters' notes. Steve Bruce transcripts copyrighted by ECM Security, LLC. Royal Dutch Navy log entries used by permission.

PART ONE

Chapter One

How Not to Burn a Car

Barman's Court is in the Old Broadway section of Everett, Massachusetts, two blocks north of the Boston line.

It's a dead-end street with four houses, two on each side. A chain strung between two concrete blocks stopped most cars from going any further. Beyond the chain was Marsh's Hill, which led to a water-filled pit a hundred feet below. It was a favorite dumping spot for stolen cars.

Al Ferrari grew up at 4 Barman's Court, the house nearest the crest of Marsh's Hill. On December 21, 1987, his eighteenth birthday, he and a friend intentionally burned a 1976 Cadillac Seville with the aim of committing insurance fraud.

They were never caught.

Reporters: You torched a car the day you turned eighteen. How did you get involved in that?

Al: It all started as a favor for a good friend of mine, Jimmy Fitzpatrick—everyone called him Jimmy Fitz. He was a couple years older than me, but our families were close, so we'd always hung around together even as little kids. He had this '76 Seville he wanted to get rid of. It was a nice car, but he was way behind on the payments, so it had to go.

The idea was simple: burn the Caddy, report it stolen, collect the money, pay off the loan. But because it was right around Christmas, Jimmy also planned on putting in a claim for a bunch of presents he had recently bought and were supposedly in the trunk. He had all the receipts, dated and in alphabetical order, ready to show when the time came to file the claim. I thought that was cool.

He offered me $100 to help him and I admit I thought about it for some time. I knew it was not going to be like buying weed or getting someone over 21 to buy booze for you or even just riding in a stolen car. This would be a real crime. And while never in a million years did I dream it would lead to everything that's happened to me since, to be honest, at the time, I didn't really want the money. Jimmy was a good friend and he asked me to give him a hand and I agreed. Where we grew up, that's what you did.

I went on a scouting mission to find a place to do the deed. I finally came across one in the leafy Town of Melrose, about 20 minutes north of Everett. There was a big state forest there that had a dirt path running through it; it was just wide enough to drive a car on. An even smaller path off this one led to a clearing about a quarter mile in. It was where the state workers burned their trash.

This was the perfect spot. Probably a couple acres around, surrounded by trees, in the middle of nowhere, but still close enough to the main road for a getaway. Jimmy and I agreed on the location. All we had to do was pick a night and, happy birthday to me, we were ready to go.

But there's one thing I've learned over the years: when you're up to monkey business like this, there's always a complication. *Always.* And we had a big one that night.

The original plan was that Jimmy would drive the Caddy into the clearing and light it on fire. Then he would hustle back to the main road where I'd be waiting in my 1967 MG sportster, the original UK speed demon. It was cramped inside but was the perfect getaway car because it could really move. We figured we'd be back in Everett before the Melrose Fire Department was even called.

But in between the time we planned all this and the night of the crime, Jimmy had broken his right foot skiing. So, what was Plan B? He suggested I drive the Caddy and I start the fire and he'd wait in the MG, using his 32-pound foot cast to step on the gas and brake.

My first thought was, no way. I mean, *this* is my getaway driver?

But as he pointed out, we'd already put so much time and effort and, frankly, lots of anxiety into this thing, he just wanted to get it over with. And so did I.

So, we went with Plan B.

We switched cars earlier that day. I took the Caddy home, bought the gas, and met Jimmy at the entrance to the state park at 7 o'clock that night. We barely waved to each other when I arrived. The plan was to be cool and stay quiet. But then Jimmy started beeping the horn at me.

I couldn't imagine what he wanted. I parked quick and ran over to the MG.

He was sitting there, smoking a cigarette, calm as hell. He asked me: "How are you going to light it?"

It was funny, in all the planning we'd never discussed how I would actually light the fire because up until a few days ago, Jimmy was going to do the act. But I assured him now that I knew how to do it.

"I'm going to pour all the gas inside the car," I told him. "Then, I'm going to roll down the driver's side window, light a match and throw it in."

I remember Jimmy flipped his cigarette away in disgust. Suddenly he was not so cool.

"What are you stupid or what?" he hissed at me. "If you do that, you'll get your ass torched, too."

I started to tell him that's how I'd seen it done a bunch of times on TV, but he just kept on.

"Look, this is how you burn a car," he said, slowly settling down. "You pour in the gas and roll down all the windows but only halfway. Then find a softball-sized rock, wrap a rag around it and put gas on the rag. Back up a good distance from the car, twenty feet or so, then light the rag and throw the rock with enough force that you hit the car. Remember, you don't have to get it into any of the open windows or anything. Just make sure you *hit* the damn thing."

To tell you the truth, I wasn't convinced his way was going to work any better than mine. But again, by then, I just wanted to get it over with.

So, he made me promise that's the way I'd do it.

I got back in the Caddy and drove into the state park and onto the dirt road. I'll never forget thinking as I crawled along, *this seems a lot further than I remember.* It was like I was driving forever, all in complete darkness. But I finally found the cut-off to the clearing where the state workers had their burn pits, and thank God, it was just as wide open as I remembered. It was at least the size of a little league ballpark, probably bigger. Because we had no interest in starting a forest fire, I couldn't imagine a better place.

It had started to snow, and I remember thinking, I hope the snow doesn't put the fire out. I parked the Caddy in the middle of the clearing, next to one of the state workers' trash heaps. I found a softball-sized rock and got a rag from the trunk. I'd bought five gallons of gas that morning, putting them in five one-gallon water jugs. I would have bought ten gallons if I'd had the money; as it was, I was worried I didn't buy enough. I remember thinking five gallons would have to do.

I emptied the gas inside the car and saved a little for the rag. I rolled down the windows halfway like Jimmy said, counted off twenty feet and lit the rag. Then, like a pitcher in the stretch, I wound up and threw the flaming rock towards the car.

The most astonishing thing happened next. The rock made it maybe halfway to the Caddy when suddenly—oh yes, *kaboom!*—there was a tremendous explosion. I was blown back at least ten feet and came down hard on my back. It stunned me for a few seconds. I remember my hands moving involuntarily like in a dream or something. It was fucked up and very scary.

Meanwhile the Caddy had gone about ten feet in the air, flipped over, and come down on its roof, all in a ball of flame. This caused a second, even bigger explosion, sending pieces of shattered glass, engine parts and chrome flying in every direction. It was like a war zone. I remember trying to block my ears, but they still hurt. It was that loud.

I realized two things at that moment. First, five gallons of gas had been *way* too much; a half gallon would have been plenty. And second, as if this were some big science experiment gone wrong, it turned out Jimmy knew what he'd been talking about: what explodes is not the gasoline but the gasoline vapors. And it's the concussion that kills you, not the flames.

I checked my extremities to see if a certain something was missing or on fire, but everything seemed still in place. My eyebrows were gone though, burned right off. My glasses were also missing, and I had a mouth-full of dirt and ash. I rubbed my face and found dozens of tiny shards of hot metal burned into my cheeks and brow.

I rolled over on my stomach and crawled around trying to find my glasses. But the flames were right in front of me, and it was getting frigging hot.

I finally stopped and just looked at the burning car, praying the blaze would settle down. But the opposite was true. All the trash heaps nearby had ignited by now and much of the grass around the clearing was on fire, too. Then, right on cue, a sharp gust of wind carried a cloud of embers from the burning trash heaps into the trees beyond. Within seconds, I could see small fires starting in the dried leaves underneath the branches.

I was wet, covered in dirt, brow-less and almost blind, but I knew I had to get out of there.

So, I jumped up and started running as fast as I could.

I'd thought the dirt path leading to the clearing had seemed long on the way in—it seemed ten times longer on the way out.

It was snowing like crazy by now and the ground was slippery. I knew it was just a matter of time, and sure enough, I was halfway down the path when my feet went out from under me and I fell on my face.

It didn't hurt at first, but only because something even worse had happened. The front of my jeans, from the crotch to the knees, had caught a branch or something and had ripped down both legs. They were torn so evenly, it looked like they'd been cut by a tailor.

Now, ripped pants, wet and dirty—how the hell was I going to get back in my house?

But even in those hairy moments, I knew the immediate goal was to reach the main road where Jimmy was waiting. So, I started hobbling along and eventually I heard a beautiful sound coming out of the snow and the dark. The purring of my MG's engine, just waiting for daddy.

It got louder the faster I moved. My thoughts now were of somehow using the car's heater to dry my pants, maybe staple them back together just enough to get past my parents. You know, maybe it won't be that bad.

That's when I heard the MG's purr turn into a roar. I was stunned. I knew that sound, too.

A few seconds later, I stumbled out to the main road, just in time to see my good buddy Jimmy drive away...

I glanced over my shoulder and was sure I saw the reason why. It looked like the entire state park was on fire. The smoke was incredible, and the flames were higher than the tallest trees. I was sure the glow could be seen for miles.

In that same split second, I could see the taillights of my MG getting smaller and smaller. But getting left out in the middle of Melrose, on a state highway, nearly blind, nearly burned, wet, ripped pants, no eyebrows, smelling of gasoline and having just started a forest fire—the optics were not looking good for me.

So, I screamed at the top of my lungs: "Come back here, you motherfucker!"

And somehow, Jimmy heard me.

Chapter Two

The No-Judgement Zone

Reporters: But you remained friends with Jimmy, even though he tried to leave you behind, right?

Al: Only because of what happened a few weeks later.

Trouble seemed to find me; it's been like that all my life. So, I was in Medford one day at Playstead Park shooting hoops with a few people I knew from my part-time Christmas job. When the game ended everyone dispersed except me. I had to wait for a bus to get me home. It was getting dark and of course the fucking bus is late.

I could just feel the bad vibes closing in on me, that feeling of being in a neighborhood that wasn't my own.

That's when a couple Medford kids approached me and started giving me shit. One thing led to another, and they jumped me. This was right at the busy intersection of Playstead Road and High Street, five o'clock at night. People driving by, people stopped at the traffic light. Lots of people around watching these two clowns beat the crap out of me.

It ended when the light changed, and I heard a car screech up, scaring the kids away. I thought it was the cops. But it was Jimmy. He was driving home from work—in his new car, by the way—and saw the whole thing while he was stopped at the red light.

It was the first time I'd seen him since that night in Melrose. I'm Sicilian, I live by a certain set of rules, and so there was no way I was going to be his friend after that. He'd insisted his foot cast got stuck between the gas pedal and the floorboard. But I didn't care. I dropped him off that night, got by my parents ripped pants and all and we hadn't spoken since.

He was shocked to come upon me many blocks from home, getting my ass kicked in the gutter. But he was also very pissed. I know I looked bad. I was bruised and cut and again with ripped pants, but I had no broken bones, and didn't need a hospital. So, I got in his car and for the next thirty minutes, we drove around looking for the kids who'd jumped me, but we had no luck. Jimmy finally drove me home, I thanked him and successfully snuck in my house again.

I thought that was the end of it. But a couple of days later I was hanging out in front of Kelsey's Bar in Harrington Square in Everett when Jimmy pulls up. He's lit, and very excited. I asked him what was up, and he told me he got one of the kids.

I had to think a moment. Finally, I asked him: *one of what kids?*

He said: "One of the Medford kids that beat you up. I was looking for them and caught one right at Playstead when I was coming home from work."

I was stunned. Jimmy wasn't a big guy. But he *was* a little crazy. It ran in his family.

"You beat his ass?" I asked him.

I remember him smiling, teeth stained with tobacco.

"Nope," he said. "I broke his arm with a baseball bat."

Now, I was the one in shock. "You *broke* his *arm*?"

Jimmy nodded yes and said: "Now you and I are even."

And just like that, we were friends again.

To celebrate, we drove to Kelly's Roast Beef on Revere Beach, a popular late-night hangout one town over. We knew a few people from Everett who worked there. We were parked outside most of the night with our friends coming out to talk to us on their breaks. I remember they gave us each a free sandwich and Coke.

Jimmy and I were talking like nothing ever happened. He even got me to admit that he'd probably saved my life back when we burned the car because had I done it my way, they would have found my ashes and that's about it. I also agreed that the floorboard of the MG was tight and maybe we were expecting too much from his 32-pound cast.

We were about to leave Kelly's when, out of nowhere, a kid came up to the driver's side window, and clocked Jimmy with a punch to his left eye. I thought Jimmy would lose consciousness, that's how hard this punch had landed.

But somehow, he had the presence of mind to grab onto the kid's arm when he tried to punch him again and then to hit his power window button. Up went the window, squeezing the kid's forearm just above the wrist and trapping him.

By the time I got out of the car to help, Jimmy had opened the door and had punched the kid twice, pretty flush I might add, while his arm was still stuck in the window. The kid fell backwards after the second blow, freeing himself but hitting the pavement hard. Jimmy and I started to kick the crap out of him—but then came the blue lights.

I looked up to see the black and red patrol car of the Revere Police.

My parents always told me that if I ever got arrested, I should plan on spending the night in jail, because they weren't going to bail me out. Jimmy's parents had told him the same thing, plus, his dad was a cop. Everyone called him "Big Jimmy" and he was a real no nonsense-type guy. So, we knew they weren't coming for us anytime soon either.

We spent the night in the Everett lock-up, dropped off there by Revere Police. Me, Jimmy and the kid we almost beat up. His name was Franny DeMarco, a football player from the hated Medford Mustangs.

It turned out he was the older brother of the kid whose arm Jimmy broke for me.

It was strange. We spent about six hours with this guy, in close quarters, and while no one apologized to anyone, we almost became friends with him. He was just like us, doing what he had to after Jimmy had done what he felt *he* had to.

Franny got bailed out by his mother around 4AM. She arrived in slippers and curlers and smoking a butt. He didn't say goodbye or shake our hands or anything, but he proved to be a solid guy because he didn't snitch to his mom that the punk sitting over there was the one who broke her other son's arm with a baseball bat.

A couple hours later, a guy in a striped suit stopped by our cell. He looked at us through the bars and just shook his head. The Everett lock-up was attached to the old central court and this guy looked like a lawyer. He asked the court officer what we were in for. The CO was a big Black guy, and you just knew he'd been dealing with knuckleheads like us for years. He told striped suit: disturbing the peace. That was the first time we'd heard what we were being charged with.

The guy walked away, but he was back a few minutes later carrying a box full of rags and two cans of car wax. He gave them to the CO then left again.

The CO grabbed the keys and opened our cell.

"We're free?" Jimmy asked him.

He handed us the box of rags and polish and said: "Follow me…"

He led us to the courthouse's garage. It was a grubby little place but tucked in the far corner was a big, black Cadillac Fleetwood, like something a funeral home would drive.

He pointed to the Caddy and said: "That's the judge's car. Wax it until I can see rainbows."

***

Two hours later it was our turn to go to morning court. Because no one had bailed us out, we had to be formally charged.

That's when my parents finally showed up. Both were beyond angry. But before I even got to talk to them, the same CO took them aside and basically told them to sit tight. He knew the drill.

We were the first case on the docket, Judge Walter Troy presiding. He was some old dude with white hair and he knew we'd just waxed his car. But he decided to display his acting skills, pretending like he was pissed. He scolded us for the fight, said punks like us were what was wrong with this country because we promoted violence. His face was turning red, and I remember a vein bulging out of his brow. I seriously thought it was going to pop.

But then, I think the CO gave him the high sign or something, because for whatever reason, Judge Troy suddenly went schizoid and switched tracks. He told us he thought we were good kids despite all the crap we'd just done and that in his wisdom, the court was letting us off with a warning.

It was an academy award performance.

Hope you liked the wax job, Mister Brando.

Chapter Three

Hashing it Out

Reporters: You had a difficult time one night involving a large amount of hashish and you've said you feel that event more than anything else affected your mental processes and everything that happened to you afterwards. That sounds extreme. Can you tell us about all that?

Al: As soon as my girlfriend Sue got out of high school, we got an apartment and moved in together. It was near North Broadway in Everett, about five minutes from where I grew up.

At this point, Jimmy and I were working at the same place: Palumbo Printing of Malden. We were shufflers. We'd move these huge rolls of paper from the printing presses to cutting rooms and then re-load the presses with more paper. The boss was a super-asshole, but other than that, it was a good job.

Every September I would buy an ounce of hash because that's when it was usually available. By coincidence, one day in September the girl who was the office manager at Palumbo Printing gave Jimmy and me a recipe for pot brownies. It was a Friday night and I'd already bought the hash, so we went back to my place to make some brownies and get high that way for a change.

The trouble was, we had no idea what we were doing. The recipe was for weed, not hash. But I got my ounce out anyway and started slicing off thin pieces with a razorblade. We were trying to approximate how much weed would equal how much hash for what would eventually be a pan full of brownies. But every time we added up the numbers, it seemed like the brownies wouldn't be very strong if we stuck to the recipe.

We finally decided to screw the slicing. We crumbled the entire ounce into the brownie mix, stirred it and then put the pan in the oven at 350-degrees as instructed. Then we went out for a beer.

Sue was home by this time, so I'd asked her to shut off the oven when the timer pinged and to please take the brownies out to cool. She was not a fan of our culinary efforts and predicted that this, like a lot of things Jimmy and I got into, would end badly.

The timer went off and Sue took out the pan. But according to her, just by looking at it she knew we'd done something wrong. The mix had burned in some places, but was still cold, gooey and black in others. She said it looked like it came from a garbage disposal and tasted worse.

And that's what stayed with me. She said the brownies looked bad, tasted bad. They went into the freezer after that, and I practically forgot about them. Even after a month went by, I had still yet to taste them.

Another Friday night rolled around. Jimmy came over and suggested we drive up to Salisbury Beach and go drinking. Salisbury was about thirty minutes north of us and was my home away from home in my younger years. It was a lot of honky-tonk, but always hopping, lots of cool bars and girls and the beach was surprisingly nice.

I was all for going—but there was a complication: neither of us had any weed, essential for a night out. That's when I suggested we get into the brownies. So what if they tasted awful? How would we know after a few beers? Jimmy agreed.

I grabbed a knife and cut the contents of the pan into about a dozen squares. As I was doing this, Sue asked me repeatedly, "Are you sure this is a good idea?"

15

I told her not to worry, that we'd be fine.

To prove it to her, Jimmy and I ate three brownies each, right then and there, in between a couple beers. Almost a half hour later, we were still very un-stoned. Once again, I told Sue not to worry. Then we took off for Salisbury Beach.

We drove for about forty minutes and on arrival, headed directly to the Kon Tiki Lounge, one of the nicer places there. We took up a couple of stools and started drinking beer. Almost an hour and a half had passed since we ate the brownies, and we still felt no effects.

This was baffling. We talked about how when you cook something, it loses its potency. Like alcohol when it's thrown onto something being cooked. It all burns away. Maybe it's the same with marijuana. Then why do pot brownies exist, Einstein? Well, have you ever heard of *hash* brownies? No, because hash is *so* concentrated it cooks away just like alcohol.

After ten minutes of this jabberwocky, I was convinced I'd burned away a hundred bucks worth of hash and was left with nothing.

We changed the subject to Jimmy's weekend job. One of his relatives owned a farm in Lexington that trained and boarded trotters. Jimmy worked there Saturdays and Sundays and got paid good money. But the job was nothing like Palumbo's Printing. It was more varied, let's say. For instance, early the next morning Jimmy had to bring one of his farm's female horses to another farm nearby to be mated. These things could sometimes take hours and because both owners wanted to know every little detail of the process, Jimmy would be taking notes and videotaping the entire event.

We started talking about horses having sex. Were there cute female horses, or will the male horse just fuck anything with four hooves? That kind of stuff—and that should have been clue number one, because

16

sometime during the horse-coitus discussion I started to sweat like a pig.

The world around me started bending and melting away. I turned to Jimmy. He had his head down on the bar with his hands covering his ears. I thought we'd just been talking, but he looked asleep. Suddenly everyone around us looked like aliens from Star Wars. I seriously thought we'd stumbled into a costume party.

We somehow ordered two more beers, hoping the alcohol would calm us down and not cook away. But truthfully, with each passing moment, we were getting more and more fucked up—and not in a good way. Sue had been right; this couldn't help but end badly.

Pretty soon I could barely move, never mind drink. But suddenly Jimmy starts talking about horses fucking again. All he really said was: "I think they like the gray ones best..." but at that point we broke into laughing fits so loud the bartender walked over to us and said: "You two are shut off."

I remember this guy was a real Disco Dan, chest hair, chains and all. But clearly it was not the time to get in a beef with him—or anyone.

I plunged ahead anyway.

"We've only had two beers each," I told him. "And we haven't even finished the second one yet."

He didn't care. To him we were just two laughing idiots—and we were making the other customers uncomfortable.

He said, "Finish your beers...quietly...or you're out."

We sat there in silence for the next few minutes, nursing our beers. But then Jimmy leaned over and whispered: "I think some of the girl horses are hot, but they've got to wash them down first."

I couldn't believe he said it, but he did and suddenly I'm laughing so hard I can't catch my breath. I'm coughing and hacking, doubled over on my seat. That was it for Danny the bartender. He took our beers away and told us to get out.

The problem was, neither of us could walk. I couldn't feel my legs, it was like half my body had disappeared. I had to grab onto the bar just to stand up. Jimmy was the same way, and it looked like a mile to the door.

I remember holding on the entire length of the wall to get out. It was bad. Everything was spinning, everyone looking at us. I imagined my heart was going to explode and I felt like I was going to vomit—both at once. We got outside somehow and just stood there shaking.

I asked Jimmy: "Has this peaked yet?"

He could barely form words at this point. "I've done acid that wasn't this bad," he managed to tell me. "It just won't stop."

Now came the real fun. We had to drive back to Everett. We found his car somehow and thank God, he got behind the wheel because I was completely useless. He started driving to the highway very slowly. Meanwhile I had my head out the window, ready to throw up at any moment.

Everything changed once we got to Interstate 95. Jimmy stopped before getting on the on-ramp and said to me: "I can't do this. I can't drive on the highway."

I told him that neither could I and that he *had* to do it. But he kept shaking his head, saying he couldn't.

We went back and forth for God knows how long, neither of us making any sense. Finally, he just yelled: "Fuck it!" and hit the accelerator.

The next thing I knew we were up the entrance ramp and swerving over to the passing lane going at least 100 MPH. I put my head between my knees and started begging God to make it stop.

"I've got to get it over as quick as possible," Jimmy yelled to me.

Then he let out a scream, like he suddenly had Tourette's or some-thing. I was scared shitless and very paranoid, but I kept my head down because I knew if I sat straight up, I'd barf all over the car.

But his screaming continued.

After the fourth or fifth time, I slowly lifted my head and discovered it was only when we went under an underpass that Jimmy would scream in terror. I asked him what the fuck was going on and he told me that every time we came to an underpass, he saw a dragon and we were about to drive into its mouth, at which point the damn thing would col-lapse on us. So, every time we came to one, Jimmy was closing his eyes, screaming, and then booting it to a hundred plus until we got on the other side. It was like being in a bad dream where you can't move, can't cry out. I was ready for the car to hit something at any moment.

But, astonishingly enough, after about thirty minutes, we were able to get off Interstate 95 in one piece. But it was only to find ourselves on Route 1, possibly the most erratically designed, most dangerous highway in America.

And more underpasses brought more screaming.

That's how it was the rest of the way home.

After a dozen more panic attacks, but miraculously no vomit, we made it back to my place. Jimmy insisted on sleeping out in the car and I didn't argue with him. I went inside and staggered into the bedroom. Sue had fallen asleep studying for a college entrance exam that she had the following morning. She was going for her degree in education at the time.

I was a disaster. I was trying to get undressed the best I could, but I was all over the place, bumping into the wall, then falling down.

Sue woke up and asked if I was okay.

All I returned was a blank stare, I had no words.

"That's what I thought," she said. "Just sleep it off."

So, I plopped myself down and figured after some decent shut-eye our night in Salisbury would be nothing more than a bad memory.

But I was wrong.

When I woke up the next morning, the room was spinning like a top. I tried to stand up but kept losing my balance and falling over. I still felt like I had to vomit, and my head was ready to explode.

I couldn't believe it, I was just as fucked up now as I was when I went to bed, maybe even more so. And as Sue had already left to take her test, I was home alone to face the horror.

It was Saturday and I stayed on the couch most of the day, praying to God to make it stop. I gave Him my word that day, and I'm proud to say that I kept it. I never ate hash again. I mean, I smoked it, of course, but never ingested it, once was enough.

Saturday turned to Sunday, and nothing had changed in my condition. I was still wrecked that morning. Sue did her best to help me out, but there was nothing she could do. As the clock ticked away, I wondered if I should go to the hospital for some help. Would a blood transfusion make it go away?

Finally, by late Sunday afternoon the hash began to wear off. I still had trouble walking and talking or making any sense, but at least I could function somewhat like a human being again.

So yes, I can tell you in all honesty I was never the same after that. My thought processes never quite lined up like they had before. But it's not an entirely bad thing.

Reporters: In what way?

Al: Since then, I feel like I have just a little bit more luck than the average person.

Reporters: How is that not an entirely good thing?

Al: Because there's two kinds of luck, good and bad. And if you want to be able to enjoy the good luck, you have to be able to take the bad, or at least identify it. It seems to go both ways in almost equal measures, just a little more so for me.

Reporters: How did Jimmy make it through the rest of that lost weekend?

Al: I went to work on Monday, still woozy, but presentable. I met up with Jimmy, and he assured me that was the most loaded up he'd ever been. But he hadn't spent the weekend curled up in a fetal position on his living room couch praying to make it stop. It had been much worse for him.

He told me he woke up that Saturday morning, still loaded, still in a daze and very nauseated. He went down to the kitchen where his mom had made him breakfast. But when he took a bite of the toast, it stuck to the roof of his mouth because his mouth was so dry. He had to get it out with a spoon. His mother asked him what the hell was wrong with him. "I had a bad night," he told her.

From breakfast he went and collected his girl horse and drove to the stud farm in Lincoln, Mass., about 20 miles away. The horse was washed, groomed, and weighed and then brought to an extra-large paddock. Jimmy set up his video camera near the door and started a new page in his notebook.

Then the farm's stud was brought in, the love birds were put together, and Jimmy watched them have sloppy wet horse-sex for the
next six hours.

Chapter Four

Frankie the Rose

Recorded October 29, 1991, at the offices of Pink Strongbox Productions, Beverly Hills, Ca. Interview with Officer Steve Bruce retired, Everett Police Department.

Reporters: How did you first meet Al Ferrari?

Steve Bruce: It started with a case my partner Joey Kelly and I picked up on March 17 of that year. It was Saint Patrick's Day and I remember it was freezing out. We got a call from a community housing cop working in Glendale Heights in Everett that an upscale vehicle had been parked in the neighborhood for a couple days and he thought it might be stolen.

The Heights was the worst part of Everett. Basically, six blocks of projects surrounded by abandoned buildings and empty lots. We used to call it The Bronx. A nice car sitting there unattended for any length of time would raise suspicions.

The vehicle in question turned out to be a 1961 Lincoln Continental. It was parked in front of a small housing project across from a large empty lot and it looked very out of place. It was all black with lots of chrome, and when we rolled up on it, I remember thinking it looked like the car JFK was shot in.

We'd done the stolen-car drill hundreds of times. The first step was to put the license plate into the system and see who the car belonged to. This thing was almost a collectible, and Joey and I talked about how much it was probably worth. So, when we ran the plate, we were sure it would bounce back as stolen from an address in Boston's Back Bay or another rich neighborhood nearby. Punks dropping off their crap in Everett once they were done playing with it.

But we were wrong. The number came back not as stolen—but as part of a missing person's case. The owner was Frances Sinatra Rosario. He'd been missing for 48 hours. Making it even more interesting, he had a rap sheet that indicated he worked for the Marcello crime family of the North End of Boston.

At that point, it got a little more serious.

For us, step two was to do a visual search of the vehicle. I remember we were immediately freezing our asses off as soon as we got out of our squad car. Joey tried all the doors, but they were locked, and that sucked because it's a lot easier when they're not locked up.

We didn't see anything in our through-the-windows observation of the front and backseat, so we called Missing Persons and told them what had transpired. They said a search warrant was on the way and that we should call Special Services to come out and bust the locks. I remember when the Special Service guys showed up, they had coffee, and we didn't.

They broke into the car, but there was nothing to be found inside. The interior was just like the exterior, nicely done and well-maintained.

So now it comes time to pop the trunk. We suspect this Rosario guy is in there, but we don't know for sure. It was too cold to leave any smell. But that was the problem. Differences in temperature and gases released by a dead body can do weird things in a confined area. In this case, when you popped the trunk, you might be faced with a jack-in-the-box situation.

And no one wanted that.

So, we opened the trunk—slowly—but right away comes this quick blast of foul air. We know it all too well. Oh yeah, DOA…

But because its *freezing* cold, the stink basically dissipates. But now we're looking down at this guy in the trunk. He's a big guy, he's in a nice suit and he's frozen solid. He's also full of holes. His wig is hanging half off, and it had holes in it too.

We laughed—all of us. It's never *really* funny in these situations, but this one was just weird enough to get us going. Then we called it in, and two crime scene detectives showed up ten minutes later. Joey and I knew them both.

They took one look at the stiff and just nodded. "Frankie the Rose," one told us. "Misplaced about fifty grand of the Marcellos' money a few days ago. Looks like their HR department finally got in touch with him."

They started taking pictures and doing all this other stuff, including trying to see how many times the guy had been shot and where. They're gently pushing and prodding around a bit, but The Rose was frozen like a ham. Finally, one of the detectives puts on these thick rubber gloves and drills his finger right into the fattest part of the guy's stomach. He begins to push really hard—and out pops a bullet.

I remember the guy caught it in mid-air, sniffed it, then said: "Hmm, garlic…"

About ten minutes later, our sergeant shows up with a warrant to toss the car, which would then allow us to remove the body. That meant we've somehow got to get Frankie out of the trunk. But he's basically twisted into the shape of a pretzel. A frozen pretzel and an incredibly massive one. To get him up on a gurney, we must straighten him out first.

So, it's me, Joey and the detectives and the Special Services guys and we're all twisting him this way and that. But we can hear this tearing, crunching noise every time we bent him too far. It was grotesque, but we finally got him on the gurney.

Now this is where we have to properly search this guy and when it came to searching a DOA's person, that was up to the first cops on the scene. This was important because Joey and I used to go back and forth as to who does the searching. You know, I search one, next time, it's your turn—and believe me we kept close track of who's turn it was, because no one ever wanted to do it. You're literally going through the pockets of a dead person, and whatever you find sure ain't going to do them any good anymore and you wonder why they had it on them in the first place. It's spooky. And the one thing I remember about this guy was that he had this giant pinky ring on. Real tacky but no surprise, right?

Anyway, it was my turn to do the search and that meant I had to get his wallet, maybe his keys and other personal effects—plus I had to take off that ring. And pulling a ring off in these circumstances, especially the cold and that sudden change in temperature—sometimes not just the ring comes off.

I closed my eyes and gave it a yank and, damn, it slid right off into my hand. It was beautiful. Too beautiful. I opened my eyes to see yes, I had the ring, but also his pinky and the finger next to it. They looked like two little bloody popsicles, bent and broken at the knuckles. It was almost big vom time for me. I tossed them away but luckily, they landed in the snow, which, by procedure, was a good place for them.

We dropped the ring in our evidence bag and then one of the detectives put the severed fingers into another bag he'd filled with snow. I was still close to throwing up and all I could remember was the sergeant, watching all this from his car, drinking a cup of coffee, heat on, with his driver, laughing at us.

I finally got my shit together and retrieved the dead guy's wallet, which also had bullet holes in it, but no money. I found a small address book which the detectives confiscated immediately.

And that was about it. The bus arrived; that's what we call an ambulance. We helped the EMTs put Frankie in the back and off they went. Then the Special Services guys and detectives left, and so did the sergeant.

Case closed. All we had to do now was go back to the station and do the paperwork, which was always a pain in the ass but at least we'd be warm. By this time, the department's tow truck had shown up. It was a typical wrecker except it was painted in Everett's Police colors and had revolving lights on its roof. We also knew these guys.

They hooked up the Continental from the front, and the driver started lifting it slowly; he knew this was not some chump car. Meanwhile, his assistant went around to the back to make sure the rear fender wouldn't be dragging on the ground once they started to move.

We were back in our car by this time, but I remember hearing the assistant say: "Holy crap… did you guys search the trunk?"

We hadn't. We'd searched *inside* of the car and we'd searched the DOA, but as soon as we'd twisted him out of the trunk, all the attention stayed on him. Besides, forensics was going to go over the entire car as soon as it got to the compound.

Joey and I got back out of our warm squad car and went back to the rear of the Continental. The tow truck guy had lifted a piece of the trunk's floor to reveal a round space where the car's spare tire would be kept.

There was no tire. But there was a suitcase full of cash.

Just a little under $50,000.

27

***

Twenty minutes later, everyone who'd left the scene—the detectives, Special Services and our sergeant—had returned. And our lieutenant and the district captain were also there. We were now just two little Indians in the middle of a lot of chiefs. Even the tow truck guys were getting more of the attention from the Brass.

It went on like this for a while, the higher-ups talking amongst themselves. Then we saw the lieutenant pull our sergeant aside for a private conversation, then they both spoke to the detectives and finally the district captain. We could see they were clearly talking about us. Finally, the sergeant called us over. He told us to go on our meal break now and that we would be returning here to the scene in about an hour.

Why?

He said we'd find out when it was our turn to know.

I remember we went to Kelsey's in Harrington Square and talked about why we were going back to the Heights. We figured they were going to put us on surveillance of the car, but the question was, what brought up their reluctance to tow it in the first place? We found out later that the Marcello Family was still looking for their fifty grand—and on the instructions from the FBI, the Everett Police put out a typical all-points abandoned car report on the Continental, one of about a dozen they dealt with every day. This one had a very distinct description of the vehicle, highlighting its high-vintage quality, but with no mention of a body being found inside.

Then the FBI replaced the real fifty grand with fifty grand in old, marked bills, and put the suitcase back inside the trunk along with four massive green dye explosive packets. The Feds were confident news of the abandoned Continental would leak out of the Boston Police

Department and go right to the Marcellos. The plan was to put some eyes on the car for the night, just to see if anyone came back, poking around.

Cool plan, yes. But poor execution is always where these things get fucked up. Instead of having the FBI, or the State Police anti-crime unit or maybe even Special Services with all their SWAT toys sit on the car, they left the surveillance to me and Joey. We were told to pick up an unmarked car at the station after our break and then watch the Continental all night—a busted shift for us—and report in with anything unusual.

But it didn't even get that far.

About thirty minutes after we left the scene for our meal break, the detective squad put the fake money in the trunk but then took off, leaving the tow truck guys there alone until we came back in the unmarked car.

Now to hear the tow truck guys tell it, they were ordered back to their garage by their higher command because some asshole selectman's car had broken down at City Hall and he wanted it towed for free. Up to that point we'd never heard of the tow truck guys being ordered to go anywhere; they just weren't that high up on the food chain.

But they radioed us, told us the situation and asked what our ETA was. We told them we were sixty seconds away and that we'd relieve them momentarily. They radioed us a Roger, but sixty seconds later when we arrived, they were gone.

And so was the Continental.

For the first ten minutes after that, we thought the tow truck guys had mistakenly taken it with them. When that turned out not to be the case, the whole department went nuts. This had the makings of a major embarrassment for everyone involved so another all-points bulletin was launched, this time to look for a missing car that was involved in a homicide.

All the urgency didn't translate to the detective squad, though. They were convinced the Continental was gone for good. They believed the Marcellos had fallen for the ruse, had returned to where they'd dumped the car to retrieve the $50,000 they'd stupidly left behind in the first place, and by the chance of incredibly good timing, got there in the sixty seconds that no one had eyes-on it and drove it away. A massive fuck up.

The Brass was freaking out, the FBI had vanished, and the detective squad was calling for the tow truck guys to be fired.

But Joey and I knew better. Most seasoned mobsters weren't morons, but you could make a good case that a lot of the low-level ones were. To so cleanly snatch anything in such a narrow span of time in that part of town just wasn't like them. This had been done by an expert. Someone who could boost a car in the blink of an eye.

It was close to midnight by now and the car had been missing for about an hour. Once we were able to get out of the station house, which was heated, but still not a good place to be at that moment, we drove directly to Barman's Court and Marsh's Hill, that ideal place for dumping cars.

The moment we got there we saw a figure standing in the brush near the edge of the hill, taking a piss. We put a light on him. He was eighteen or so and looked like he'd been dipped in green paint.

He turned on our command, and we got out, keeping him in the light.

My first question to him was: "Why are you covered in green?"

He answered, "Because I'm going to the Saint Patrick's Day parade in Southie tomorrow…"

Joey and I both shook our heads. "That was yesterday, genius," Joey told him. "Where do you live? The North End? Or East Boston?"

The kid shook his head, pointed to the last house on the dead-end street and said: "My family lives right over there."

Two steps away from taking a leak inside? Another mastermind, I thought. As Joey applied the cuffs, I asked the kid his name.

He said: "Al Ferrari…"

We had to hold him until the detectives got there and found what everyone was looking for at the bottom of Marsh's Hill. We told Al he was a suspect in a grand theft auto case, but nothing beyond that. It would be up to the detectives to decide his fate from there.

It was about 1 A.M. when the squad finally arrived, found the Lincoln and took Al into custody. But, unlike us, they were convinced Al was a low-level associate working for the Marcellos—and they planned an all-out assault to get him to crack.

But it took them barely ten minutes to realize Al was not connected to the Mob. They could just tell; it was something that came along with the job. He was just a young kid with a talent for swiping cars and whose own car had broken down in the Heights and, well, it was cold and he was broke—and a long way from home.

Now had the Marcellos had an eye on the car as the detective squad wanted them to—and *they* saw Al in the act, he might have wound up perforated and in the trunk as well. But he had a fair amount of good luck that night, and as I would find out, that seemed to happen to him a lot.

But all luck, good or bad, must end at some point and Al's good luck ended just before he pushed the big car over the edge of Marsh's Hill. He happened to look in the trunk and see the suitcase stuffed with stacks of wrapped hundred-dollar bills. Instinct told him to grab one, just to make sure what he was seeing was real. One quick explosion was followed by three others and in a matter of seconds, Al was covered in green dye, head to toe, mouth, nose, ears, everything including the lenses of his glasses, without which he was sightless.

But props to him, he kept his wits about him long enough to blindly push the car over the edge and into the water pit below—and *then* he decided to take a leak. That's when we came upon him.

When we heard the detectives had hit a foul ball, I spoke to the prosecutor the next day and let him know Al seemed genuinely harmless and was just a dopey kid who wanted to get the hell out of the Heights on a cold night. He said he'd take it under advisement. And even though the Continental was recovered from the bottom of Marsh's Hill and finally brought to the holding compound, no one ever claimed it. No one ever came looking for the fifty grand. So, the case went away.

Six months passed by the time Al came up for trial. By that time, the charges had been reduced to simple car theft, based on the age of the Continental. It being his first offense, or more accurately, the first time he'd been caught, his public defender and the prosecutor worked out a deal for a six-month sentence, all of it suspended. If he stayed out of trouble for two years, his record would be wiped clean. It was the City of Everett's basic agreement for all first-time youthful offenders.

But, as I was told later, the trial itself went wrong quickly. Complication number one: the presiding judge was Justice Walter Troy, the same loony-toon who had Al and Jimmy Fitz wax his car before he scared the crap out of them and then just as quickly let them go, scot-free.

Al said he recognized the guy by the vein bulging out of his forehead.

The judge read over both arguments and then viewed the evidence folder, and this was where a second complication came in. The judge saw a picture of the Lincoln and for the first time someone recognized it for what it was: a very expensive, highly collectible car—and porn to someone who drove a simple black Caddy, with no chrome.

Judge Troy knew it was worth at least $10,000, which was a lot of scratch back then. But Al's agreement was based on the car being worth less than $1,000, which meant his crime was basically one of petty theft. Going over a grand made it literally grand theft auto and boosted his crime back up to felony status. Suddenly, he was looking at three to five years in prison and maybe as much as fifteen.

Al said his lawyer and the prosecutor tried to hammer out another agreement right there, but neither was experienced in dealing with felonies. Meanwhile, His Honor seemed obsessed with the photos of the car, reportedly looking at them over and over.

Finally, Al said the judge stared down at him strangely, like he was looking at a bug, he recalled. He saw the vein in the guy's head start to grow again.

"You?" he suddenly thundered down at Al. "I know you, don't I?"

Al said he went numb, just unable to speak. And then, just as suddenly as the last time they had met, the judge did a complete flip and went on: "Yes, I know you. You're an OK kid. I'm going to throw out this felony charge and go back to your original deal. But with these stipulations: You immediately get a job and you also report to the Department of Adult Services of Everett on a regular basis. They will monitor your progress and they will let this court know if you go out now and make something of yourself. Or if you slip up. If that happens, we'll have no other choice but for you to serve your six months in jail."

Al later told me he wrote a poem about that day, called Blindsided. Within just a few chaotic minutes and on the will of a nutty judge, he had acquired a file with the Department of Adult Services, something that, he would find, had the potential to hang around his neck for the rest of his life.

DAS was well known around Everett. It was basically a place for politicians to park cronies and relatives. DAS was supposed to be like family social services, but for adults. There was no age restriction, but Al was barely 19 when he got tied up with them for really no good reason. Most people in his first-offense situation were simply told to stay out of trouble and get a job.

It turned out, we all learned later, that Judge Troy's sister-in-law was pulling down $40,000 a year for a no-show job at—well, want to guess where?

Chapter Five

Pick up Order 86!

Reporters: How did you end up working in the funeral business?

Al: Sue had finished a year of college by that time. We'd gotten married in a quickie ceremony and she was working as a teacher's aide. But I hadn't worked for months, ever since Palumbo Printing automated their entire process and fired about twenty of us. I was unemployed when I got jammed up on the stolen car thing, so the judge basically said he'd throw out the charge if I got a job. Well, I looked just about every day for *three months* and I still hadn't found anything. It was the late 80s and the job market was tough back then.

But here was the thing: no one from DAS ever checked up on me. I called them like I was supposed to after the trial and I talked to some woman, but she said OK and that they'd be in touch. Weeks went by, but I never heard from them. So, at that point I decided to just stay low and hope it all just disappeared, like things like that sometimes do.

But then one day, everything went sideways.

We had just gotten a telephone answering machine. I woke up late that morning, way after Sue had left for school, so I heard the first message the machine ever recorded. It was the DAS. They wanted me in their offices at eight a.m. the next day with documentation proving three months of employment. I freaked out. Figuring out how to erase the message was easy, but now what am I going to do? I had no idea.

That night I went with Sue to one of her school functions; a Halloween fundraiser, to be exact. I told her about the phone message and that I was convinced I was going to jail. But she stayed cool as always and told me something would work out. I wished I shared her optimism at that moment.

It came time for dinner and Sue arranged for us to sit with another teacher's assistant, a woman named Terry O'Neil, and her husband, Johnny. He was a nice enough guy to talk to, he was into sports, like I was. As time went on, I learned he operated four funeral homes in the area as well as a crematorium.

I'm sure now that Sue talked to Terry and Terry talked to Johnny, because at the end of the night, he offered me a job at one of his businesses.

"Doing what?" I asked him.

"Picking up stiffs," he replied.

It seemed like an easy enough job.

The way Johnny described it, on most occasions one of his employees would get called to a hospital or a morgue, places where professionals would be present to lend a hand putting the deceased into the back of a hearse. Such calls were known as Fun Runs, because only one person was needed for the job and basically it was just driving from the funeral home to there and back.

But then there were the RPUs—residence pick-ups. This involved going to a home where someone had just died and transporting the body to the funeral home. These were something else entirely. They almost always required more than one person just to lift and maneuver the lifeless body around, no matter how much it weighed.

But that was usually the least of the issues.

I was the new guy, so I got all the RPUs—and none of the Fun Runs. But I'd convinced myself that it was either this job or jail. Plus, the pay was okay.

So, when DAS called again, wondering why I'd missed my appointment, I told Sue to tell them I got a job picking up dead people.

Johnny had schooled us on how to behave when we arrived for an RPU. The family of the deceased was almost always there, so he continuously reminded us to always be at our best. No swearing or insensitive remarks. Keep conversation solemn and to a minimum. And we had to allow the family at least fifteen minutes to say their goodbyes before we wheeled in the gurney and got to work.

There were actually two kinds of RPUs. Most times, we were there to pick up the body of an elderly person who'd died at home. They were usually small and frail and that made it a lot easier for us. We'd always ask for the family's permission to take the sheet beneath the one who died— and it was never a problem. Both of us would grab a side of the sheet, and on the count of three, we'd lift straight up and over and place the body on the stretcher, all in one smooth motion. Piece of cake.

But then, there were the other RPUs.

The messy ones.

My first messy was the worst. We got a call to pick up a 240-pound guy who'd committed suicide in the bathtub of a third-floor apartment. He'd put a .45 caliber in his mouth and ate the bullet—and the result *was* a mess. And there were no loved ones wanting their fifteen minutes this time. The only reason anyone knew the departed had departed was because of the smell. And let's just say the bugs and rodents had a field day.

Wayne Collie was the guy I was working with those days. He'd done a lot of messy calls, so I just followed his lead. He figured the guy in the tub was a three-part operation. First, put a body bag underneath him and lift him on top of it. Then lift the bag out of the tub and onto a second body bag on the floor. Then slip him and the two bags into a third bag, tie it up and get the hell out of there.

But we acted in haste, totally because the place was like a mini-house of horrors. Roaches scurrying over everything, rat shit everywhere. The smell was so overwhelming, even Wayne was getting sick.

Two old bath towels were nearby and instead of going back down to the truck and getting the extra body bags, Wayne said, let's do the towel trick. He put one of the towels behind the dead guy's neck and had me put the other under his ankles. Then it was, you know, lift with your legs—and when we did, the dead guy came straight up, a lot easier than I would have thought. But just as we were clearing the edge of the tub, the towel around his neck ripped and down he went.

His skull hit the tiled floor and cracked open. I'll never forget that sound. Kind of a wet pop! Anything that was inside his head a second before, spilled onto the floor. A pile of bloody, oozy brains in a puddle of sickly white goo.

We'd fucked up. We should have done it the right way, but we didn't, because we were in a hurry because the place was so horrible. But as a result, one big mess just got bigger.

We had to scramble. What was the most practical way to clean this up and still maintain the poor guy's dignity, which thanks to our boss, Johnny, was important to us at the time?

We decided to split up. While Wayne looked around the bathroom for something that would be of help, I went to the kitchen to look for the same thing. But this guy had obviously lived alone. There was no broom, no dustpan. No bucket, no mop.

But there was an empty pizza box. If I tore a piece of it off, would I be able to scoop up the brain matter and place it all back into his head?

I know it's crazy to say it, but it worked perfectly. Even to the point where the back of his skull was just sticky enough that the piece of pizza box adhered to it and kept everything inside.

We took our time carrying him down the stairs. He was heavy, so that was going to happen anyway. However, the slower we went, we thought the less likely the brains would get jostled around and the pizza box would come undone.

As far as I knew, that didn't happen.

But as we were driving away, I remember Wayne saying: "If I ever need a shrink, I'm sending Johnny the bill."

Another time we got called to an old mill building in Lowell, Massachusetts, to pick up an elderly woman. It was a massive complex. There were several cops on the scene, but they were all standing around outside. I didn't know why until my partner for that day, a guy named Marty Finn, filled me in.

He first asked me to take a look at the front of the building, and to point out the one window that just didn't look right. I gave up quickly, so he directed my eyes to a particular window among dozens that was pitch black.

"That's the apartment we're going in," he said.

I asked him, "How do you know?"

He told me: "That black color is the accumulation of flies over a long period of time. That's why all the cops are outside."

What happened was, at some point over the winter, the woman turned her oven on, got her blankets and laid down on the kitchen floor about a foot from the burners. Eventually, she succumbed to the fumes and unfortunately no one found her until June. And the only reason anyone did was because her body was badly decomposed and oozed an oily substance through the floor and into the apartment below.

So, we went up there and right away saw what was left of her had melded to the linoleum floor. But we had the blanket directly under her, and though she was stuck, we were able to get about ninety percent of her into the body bag.

The ten percent that remained, though, was her head.

We were already in the kitchen, and while I looked around for a pizza box, there was none. It didn't matter, because I saw the perfect tool—a spatula. I grabbed it and scraped a fair amount until I lifted her head carefully off the floor and dropped it in the bag. I placed it where a head normally goes, and she was good to go.

Reporters: You also worked at Johnny O'Neil's crematorium?

AL: Yes, so like I mentioned, he owned four funeral homes, but also a crematorium down in Braintree, south of Boston.

Because I'd stayed at the pick-up job for longer than most, I moved up to working at the crematorium. I was apprehensive at first. Even after all I'd gone through with some really nasty RPU's, the idea of intentionally burning a body—even a dead one—just gave me the creeps. Plus, I had this idea that the place would look like a dungeon with a huge oven or something, and hunchbacks skulking around, the works.

But it paid about a third more than picking-up stiffs, so I went and saw the place and found it was just the opposite of what I'd imagined. Everything was brand new and spotless. There were two units where the bodies were cooked; each was computer-controlled. Special stacks on the roof released smoke on a timed basis, and sensors on the inside told you when the body was done.

It was an impressive operation. Plus, it was located in this industrial park, way in back of the South Shore Shopping Mall. It was a plain, square white building, right near some woods and there was even a stream nearby. We used to shoot hoops at lunch.

Like everything else that Johnny ran, there was a procedure we had to follow religiously. Cook the body for about six hours at 2,000 degrees. Then shut it down, open the door, and use a steel rake to collect the ashes. If there were bone fragments left behind, we put them into a crusher that turned them into powder. Then everything went into an urn.

That's how we did it, day after day, and with that type of efficiency. Naturally, Johnny made some good dough. He had an employee who drove around Boston to the hospitals just to pick up stiffs that were going directly to the crematorium, no funeral wanted or needed. At the end of each week, Johnny personally delivered the urns full of ashes to the families. It was a nice, little, quiet side business.

Reporters: So why was the crematorium shut down, then?

Al: That was the fault of the guy who ran the day-to-day operations for Johnny. His name was Larry. We called him Lonely Larry because he was a weirdo. Technically he was our boss, but he left us alone a lot and would always wander off somewhere by himself. We suspected he was looking at pictures of the bodies.

Anyway, he was the guy who picked up stiffs going straight from the hospital to the crematorium. To do this he drove the company van, which was a plain black Ford Econo-liner with black drapes on the windows in back and on the sides. It looked like a cut-rate hearse. Now, believe me, Larry's job was the sweetest duty in the place, but he was always fucking up or getting lost, or losing paperwork, and always coming back to the crematorium late.

Now, you should know that if a deceased was to be cremated, they would generally not be cooked in an expensive casket. There was a cardboard-type box that was suitable for burning and left very little residue. So, when Larry would make his pick-ups, the stiff was usually in one of these cardboard boxes.

Now, by Johnny's rules, there could be no more than two bodies in the company van at a time. If Larry had to haul three bodies, he'd have to call Johnny and get his okay first, that's how strict he was about these things.

Well, one day Larry got distracted, or lost, or something but he fucked up big time and without letting Johnny or anyone else know, picked up *five* bodies before heading back to the crematorium. Even more dopey, he'd stacked the cardboard boxes one on top of the other instead of laying them side by side or strapping them in somehow. Short version: the box on top wasn't securely fastened.

He was driving back to the crematorium, four hours late, and got stuck in traffic on the Tobin Bridge. It was 5 o'clock, the height of rush hour. Just before he got to the peak of the bridge, he hit his brakes too quickly, jarring the van. This caused the unsecured cardboard box on top to fall off to the side and get wedged between the other boxes on the driver's side. It took down the black window drapes with it, which allowed bridge commuters a full view of the nude corpse of a 75-year-old woman pressed up against the van's window. This lasted for about twenty minutes, in bumper-to-bumper traffic.

Larry later testified that not everyone was horrified. He said some people were driving by waving as if to say "Hello." Someone did notify the police however and they caught up to him just before he went into the Central Artery Tunnel.

The incident resulted in Boston traffic being extra fucked up for the next few hours. But the TV news channels chose not to report what had happened, judging it to be just too grotesque. Word got out anyway and that was enough for Johnny's investors. They sued Johnny in court and basically forced him to sell all the businesses and that was it.

Once it was over, I remember Johnny saying, if it had only happened on Halloween, we would have gotten away with it.

Chapter Six

The Island of Broken Tools

Reporters: So, next came your involvement in the Sears Tools Scam?

Al: Unwitting involvement.

Reporters: Can you explain how it worked?

Al: Well, for a long time, if you bought a Craftsman tool from Sears and it broke, you could return it to any Sears store, at any time, for a replacement, no receipt needed, no questions asked. The idea behind it was that Craftsman tools were so well-made, very few of them broke.

But some did; about five percent, I think I heard once. Now, remember, Sears was huge at the time, and they sold *lots* of tools just in the Boston area alone. So, at any given time this left the company with a fair amount of returned and broken tools on their hands.

I always thought they sent them off to some magical island where they were repaired and put back out on the market, good as new. The reality was Sears had a deal with a large trucking company in the Boston area to ship the broken tools to California where they'd be put on boats to China to be melted down into something else.

Every Sears' store in the Boston area had a 55-gallon drum where the broken tools were stored. They were always painted bright blue. It took about a month to fill a barrel and at some point they would be picked up by the trucking company and brought to the West Coast.

But then, some of the drums started disappearing enroute. Someone at the trucking company was stealing a dozen or so barrels at a time and then selling them to people who frequented . . . flea markets. Or auctioning them off to those people would be better phrasing. The trucking company thief began having secret, midnight auctions out in Central Mass somewhere, and flea market people in the know would show up and bid on each bright blue barrel.

There was only one rule: you couldn't look inside the barrel before buying it. You just knew that there was a drum full of broken Craftsmen tools and you had a choice of bidding on it or not. A lot of the bidders would go by weight, because if it felt really heavy, they figured there were a lot of ratchet sets and sockets and stuff inside, which is what most people wanted. So, these guys would buy up the blue barrels—unopened and unseen—and take them to the flea markets and re-sell the contents, whatever they might be.

When the stiff business closed-up, I went on unemployment for a couple months, but now I was getting bugged regularly by the DAS to find another job. As they were overly fond of telling me: no job, and I have to serve out my six months for third degree auto theft.

Sue was substitute-teaching grade school by now and she loved going to flea markets to find the tools of her trade. Her favorite was Odd Todd's Flea Market in Rowley, Mass. It was held every weekend on a farm with a huge barn and lots of open land around it. It could have been the picture on a post card. For a typical-looking New England small town, Rowley was it.

I would go to Odd Todd's with Sue but while she went about buying other teachers' junk, I'd mostly wander around looking for reconditioned auto parts or power tools. One day I became friendly with a guy there named Boomer. Buddha would have been a better nick name. He was a big round guy, little goatee, giant smile, lots of gold teeth. He was wearing a Hawaiian shirt and big straw hat, which it turned out was his usual garb.

He was an exhibitor. His display table featured some legitimately reconditioned, reasonably priced power tools; that's what caught my attention in the first place. But right beside his table was this bright blue 55-gallon drum full of broken tools.

Every once in a while someone would come along, look in the barrel and pull out a broken wrench or something. Boomer would consult the Sears catalog, inform the potential customer of the retail price and usually they'd happily buy it at half that.

"But what were they going to do with a broken tool?" I finally asked Boomer. What good could it possibly be? That's when he let me in on the secret.

Remember the Sears Craftsman warranty? Return the broken tool to any Sears and get a new one, no receipt needed, no questions asked. Quietly in on the Blue Barrel scam, these people weren't fixing the broken tools, they were returning them for free replacements which they would then use for themselves or sell brand new at a nice profit. At the very least, it was a way to get a lot of cool tools for literally half the price.

I remember Boomer saying at the time: "Hey, Sears is only going to throw this stuff away anyway..." And to a dumb kid like me at the time, that made a lot of sense.

He made me an offer. He had to miss the following weekend and as it was right before the Fourth of July, he'd been expecting a lot of business. He knew I knew my way around tools. How about if I watched the table for him that weekend? In return, he'd give me half of whatever came in.

When I asked him how much usually came in, he pulled out a wad of cash as big as his fist and showed it to me.

"And today's been a slow day so far," he said.

I was there bright and early the following Saturday morning. I'd retrieved the blue barrel full of broken tools from Boomer's storage bin, plus his display table and about a dozen reconditioned power tools to be laid out on them. I even wore a Hawaiian shirt and a straw hat for the occasion. Beach chair, umbrella and a bunch of car magazines, it was perfect.

It was also a nice summer's day, the beginning of a long Fourth of July weekend. And Boomer had been right; the flea market started filling up around nine. By ten it was packed.

I was there only about twenty minutes when I sold one of Boomer's reconditioned power saws for $100. There was fifty bucks for me right away. Then the broken tools started moving. A customer would fish inside, pull out an adjustable wrench missing its screw or a large screwdriver missing its handle. We'd consult the Bible, as Boomer called the Sears catalog, and then sell it at half that price.

That's the way the morning went. I'd made close to two hundred dollars already and this was just the first morning of my two-day stint. Everything was looking rosy.

One guy came by around noon just as I was eating my sandwich. He was kind of odd looking. He was wearing dirty mechanics' overalls and pushing a wheelbarrow *full* of old and broken tools. But he was the cleanest, most kempt mechanic I'd ever seen. His hands looked almost manicured.

He took one look inside the bright blue barrel and his eyes went wide.

He said: "Goddamn—can I buy the whole thing?"

I didn't know what to say; I had no idea how much Boomer would want for the whole barrel. The subject never came up.

I explained to the guy that it would have to be "by the book," meaning one tool at a time and we go by the catalog for the price and then cut it in half. The guy agreed and started pulling out broken tools and examining them, one by one. Right around this time, a Yuppie family came up to us. Young preppy husband and a young preppy wife pushing a kid in a million-dollar stroller.

They also stopped and the husband looked at the tools the mechanic had taken from the barrel.

"These are all Craftsman tools," the preppy said to me. "Did you know that?"

I guess I said sure. "But they're all broken," I told him, which is what Boomer told me to say if anyone came snooping around. Then I added: "Sears is just going to get rid of them anyway, right?"

As soon as those words were out of my mouth, I found myself looking at three FBI badges. The mechanic, the preppy husband and the preppy wife were all Feds. I was surprised the kid in the stroller wasn't showing me *his* badge.

The next words I remember hearing were: "You're under arrest for trafficking in illegally re-sold goods across state lines. Come with us quietly and we won't cuff you."

They brought me to the Rowley police station, which was close by, and put me in a room that they'd appropriated for interrogations. The local cops were nowhere to be seen, a good thing.

The guy in the overalls and the preppy husband sat me down and got right to the point. I'd been caught reselling broken Sears tools.

So what? I asked them and again reiterated Boomer's rationalization, that if Sears was stupid enough to throw them away anyway, what was the problem trying to sell a few?

But as it turned out, Sears wasn't *that* stupid. Just a little dim.

What happened was—and maybe what no one in on the scam even thought about—Sears eventually noticed that the number of broken tools being recycled through Boston-area Sears stores had jumped dramatically. And instead of filling up one bright blue barrel every month, some stores had to use two, and sometimes three barrels, to handle the overload. Meanwhile, smaller numbers of broken tools from Boston were showing up in California.

Sears put two and two together and got the FBI involved.

It was at that point, one of the agents called me "Boomer," and finally a few things started to fall in place. I spent the next twenty minutes explaining to them I wasn't Boomer, even though I was wearing a very Boomer-esque Hawaiian shirt and straw hat. I asked them, did they have a picture of Boomer? The preppy husband left the room, came back a few minutes later with a blurry faxed photo of Boomer. Even with the bad quality they could tell I looked nothing like the Buddha incarnate.

But all that was beside the point because I'd still been caught re-selling stolen broken tools across state lines and it was still a federal crime.

However, I had a suspicion something was off here—and I was right. After realizing I was just an innocent bystander in the whole thing—kind of—the Feds basically said they were confiscating everything, the power tools, the blue barrel and what was left inside—and any money I'd made that day.

But they also had a deal to offer me.

If I signed a non-disclosure agreement promising to keep my mouth shut about the whole thing, Sears would agree to drop the charges. I was so stunned, I asked them to repeat it. They did and added: "One time deal."

It didn't take a genius to figure out why they wanted to go easy on me—and I'm sure anyone else caught up in the Flea Market sting. Sears wasn't being big-hearted. They were embarrassed, they didn't want the bad publicity—and they sure didn't want to give anyone else any ideas.

I told them I'd sign anything, and I did. Then, not only did they let me go, they drove me back to my car and made sure it started okay. It had been such a strange, crazy day. I hadn't made any money and the Feds had confiscated all of Boomer's stuff including the blue barrel.

But at least I wasn't going to prison.

Not this time.

Chapter Seven

The Day-Old Plum Affair

Reporters: How did you get the job at the produce stand and how did that go so wrong?

Al: My friend, Jimmy Fitz called me one day. He knew what happened in Rowley and that I was out of work and how that could screw me with DAS. He said he knew this guy, Sonny, who was opening a produce stand on Hanover Street in the North End of Boston, which at the time was a huge Italian neighborhood. He was looking for people to work for him.

I almost jumped through the phone—I needed a job bad. By this time, the DAS people had made it clear their capacity for leniency with me had reached its limit. The next time I couldn't show proof of employment or if I broke any of the rules of my release agreement, I was going to jail.

But this fruit stand job would be no cake walk. Jimmy told me it would be ten-hour days of back-breaking work and he wasn't exaggerating. Starting with erecting a giant tent, right there on Hanover Street at 6 A.M, then unloading a half dozen trucks—and that was before the business even opened. And because the fire code wouldn't allow the trucks to be unloaded on Hanover Street, it had to be done on nearby Blackstone Street. That would mean carrying dozens of cases of fruits and vegetables from more than a block away, an endless exercise of back and forth.

And that was just the morning. Another four trucks arrived in the afternoon, and they had to be unloaded just as before. When the stand finally closed, a major clean up followed and then the tent had to be taken down and stored away.

I agreed with Jimmy that it sounded like a lot of work. But then he told me the good part: The gig paid $5 an hour, $50 a day. That was almost twice the minimum wage.

We both went down there the next day and Sonny hired us on the spot.

That first week was as backbreaking as advertised.

Hanover was a busy street to begin with; now it had a huge tent set up on it which only added to the chaos. Lots of horns beeping and car exhaust. The tent was always packed with customers, and sometimes it got so busy they'd enlist us, the box movers, to wait on people. This was early August, middle of the summer and believe me, it could get brutally hot down there. I was always sweaty, always sticky and constantly thirsty.

On the upside, there were always lots of cute North End girls walking around. There was a huge city pool nearby and sometimes they'd stroll past us wearing just their bathing suits, and sometimes still dripping wet. Slipping them a free piece of fruit every so often was not only allowed but encouraged by Sonny.

"Just don't go nuts with it," he would tell us. "But always use the day-old stuff. That way we don't have to dump it…"

Sonny was an interesting guy. He was right out of a Godfather movie, but a lot of people in the North End were like that back then. He was probably 40, overly tanned but handsome, and always well-dressed even though he was running a big tent in intense heat with lots of apples and oranges under it. And he was always in a hurry, always had someplace else to be. We worked with six young dudes just off the boat from Italy. As far as we knew, none of them really spoke English and when

Sonny spoke to them, it was always in Italian, always short and quick. He never really said much to us either, but neither did he bust our balls, not once. He seemed to appreciate that we were doing all the heavy lifting.

Sonny would usually stop by the tent around 7 AM and then again mid-afternoon, both times to check the till. He would meticulously count the cash against receipts, sometimes doing it twice or three times, just to make sure. Then at the end of the day, he'd appear again and count it all again. Sometimes he'd spend up to an hour, counting and recounting, making sure everything balanced out, right to the penny.

But then, after all this, he'd always do something odd. Jimmy noticed it first, then pointed it out to me. Sonny had two strongboxes, they looked like little safes, both with tiny combination locks on them. At closing time, Sonny would take about ninety percent of the day's income and put it in one strongbox he kept in the trunk of his Caddy. The remaining ten percent he put into a second strongbox—this one painted in horrible pink. He would put this strongbox on the tent's wooden floor and using a broom, would push it about five feet under the apple display and then cover it with an oversized tablecloth, the same we used when we closed-up the place. The tablecloth served to block anyone's view of what was underneath the apple case.

Then Sonny would always seem to relax a little. He would tell us to have a good night and disappear again.

After the first few days, Jimmy and I had the job down to a science. We knew when to unload something, when to pack something else, when to start cleaning up. Most times, the Italian guys would take care of the customers, and all we had to do was move stuff around and make sure they had enough plastic bags.

And there was no bullshit on payday. Sonny came by the first Friday around noon and called us over to his Caddy, double parked nearby.

He opened his trunk, opened his strongbox, took out two wads of cash and gave one to each of us.

Wow…$250, in small bills.

Up to that point, it was the most money I'd ever had at one time.

That summer would be one of the hottest on record. The North End became even more chaotic; getting to and from work from Everett I saw enough traffic for a lifetime.

But the Fruit Gig had suddenly turned into the best job I'd ever had.

But not for long…

Our downfall came about because of one, lousy day-old plum.

I was happily married, but Jimmy was still a free agent and always on the prowl. Girls we saw in the North End on a daily basis were like super models, all of them, and usually friendly or flirty or both.

Sonny knew. A free peach, a few grapes, a giant apple. Here, tell me how you like it. Fruit as an ice-breaker.

I was able to hold it together, but to Jimmy this was paradise on overload. He was a semi-handsome guy I guess, but could get very excitable around girls. And the cuter they were, the more acute his excitement would become.

One day, a late Tuesday, he finally cornered two really cute girls just as we were closing. It was raining and he had them under the tent and they all appeared in deep conversation. I was about 20 feet away and saw him give one of the girls a plum. It was like he'd handed her a piece of gold; she was immediately aglow. But then the idiot kissed her hand like some gigolo or something and the girls quickly left.

I expected to hear another of Jimmy's near-miss stories, but the opposite was true. He'd made a date with the Plum Girl, for just a little later that night. They were going to meet at the city swimming pool right down the street and then go to dinner.

But there's always a complication, right?

And in this case, there were two.

First of all, he needed me to go with him at least for the swimming pool meet, because Plum Girl's friend lived out of town, and Plum had to hang with her until her train at nearby North Station left at 7:26. I was OK with that. I'd been Jimmy's wingman more than a few times, and frankly, the job never lasted too long. It was always just a matter of a few minutes before Jimmy said something dumb and she turned into a ghost and disappeared.

Complication number two: neither of us had any money. My first week's pay went into the bank. Jimmy had spent most of his on a Fender Stratocaster. A beautiful guitar; too bad he couldn't play a note. The rest was under his bed at home.

It took Jimmy about a minute to come up with a plan. He could borrow the money from Sonny's second strongbox, the pink one he hid under the apple stand.

It was a very bad idea of course, but details like that never bothered Jimmy Fitz.

"How will he even know it's gone?" he kept saying to me, claiming he knew Sonny put it there just so they'd have change for the cash register for the following day. "We'll get here before he does tomorrow morning and replace it. He'll *never* know."

I'd done a lot of stupid things with Jimmy, mostly because I thought that's what friends do. So even though every ounce of me wanted to say no, I agreed to help him grab some money and then walk down to the swimming pool until 7:26 train time. Then I was climbing into my car, driving home and leaving him on his own.

And that was okay with him.

We fished out the second strongbox from beneath the apple cart. Only at that moment did we think it might be locked or that we'd need a key or a combination, but that was not a problem. The strong box's tiny combination was broken. All we had to do was jiggle the handle and it popped open to reveal what looked like about a thousand dollars in tens and twenties inside.

But now, how much to take? Dinner for two in the North End? I thought fifty bucks would be way more than enough.

Jimmy took a $100.

The girls never came, of course.

We sat on a park bench right next to the pool as instructed by Plum Girl, but they were no-shows. Just about the time they were supposed to be there, however, three sketchy characters arrived in their place and seemed to be circling us.

The North End was full of bad characters back then, but this didn't bother Jimmy. He had a face that just screamed Don't Fuck With Me, and most people didn't. I felt like Tonto or Robin or someone as the three guys walked right by us and Jimmy just stared them down—and they kept on walking.

Finally admitting defeat and that the Plum Girl had duped him, I remember Jimmy was philosophical about it.

"I've been working in the sun all day and I smell like crap," he'd said. "I would rather be cleaned up when I go out on a date."

We walked back to the fruit stand, intent on returning the money to the pink strongbox and then finally getting out of town.

Jimmy used the broom to fish it out, but when we opened the broken lid we discovered the strongbox was empty. The other $900 was gone.

That was a *long* ride home.

We were equal parts terrified and just plain stumped.

Where did the rest of Sonny's hidden money go?

Jimmy was sure Plum Girl and her friend stole it, but how would they even know anything about it? Besides, a bigger problem loomed for us. Would Sonny suspect me and Jimmy of stealing it? We couldn't imagine any of the Italian dudes doing it. They were like monks—and Sonny knew that. That meant the suspicion might fall on us.

If we thought the ride home was long, fighting the traffic back in the next morning was brutal.

We wanted to get there before Sonny, but we hit tie-ups every-where—like the universe was against us—and he was already there when we arrived. The pink strongbox was right in front of him and it was still empty.

I'd expected Sonny to be in an absolute rage, but this was not the case. He looked as always, well-dressed, well-groomed, well-tanned and very calm.

This was Jimmy's show, so I let him approach the boss first. In his own roundabout way, he explained what happened with the Plum Girl and then showed him the $100 he'd taken.

"And we have no idea where the rest of it went," he said at the end.

At first, Sonny seemed confused. He looked at the $100 and then back at Jimmy. And that's when I finally saw the rage come out.

He threw Jimmy up against the apple stand. "What do you mean?"

Jimmy explained the whole thing again—and only then did Sonny realize what had happened.

"Are you saying this box was short a hundred dollars last night?" he demanded to know.

Now it was our time to be confused. It appeared Sonny wasn't so much concerned that there was no money left in the strongbox but that the amount he put in there the night before was missing a hundred dol-lars.

Still, Jimmy said yes.

"Do you realize what you've done, you punk?" Sonny screamed at him. Then, he threw the empty strongbox away, jumped in his Caddy and roared off.

It took one of the Italian guys to tell us what the fuck was going on.

His name was Emilio and of the six original bambinos, he was the one who could speak English the best, which was next to nothing at all. But it didn't matter, what he explained to us wasn't that complex.

The strongbox in Sonny's Caddy contained the operating funds for the fruit stand. The contents of the pink strongbox was a vig—for *vigorish*. A ten percent payment to someone for some reason, usually in sports betting, but sometimes meaning someone getting ten percent of someone else's pie. Emilio explained the pink safe was picked up and cleaned out every night by someone in the know.

It was crystal clear to me: Sonny was using ten percent of the proceeds from the produce stand to pay someone he owed. But with the strongbox being light $100, it could mean big trouble because legitimate people usually aren't involved in strongboxes, or the *vigorish* or picking up money in the middle of the night. Sonny might catch a beating, or worse.

That meant, at that moment, on that summer's morning, two numbskulls like us were facing the reality that we might be the reason our boss was going to get whacked. DAS was definitely not going to like this one.

Jimmy went into attack mode. He asked the Emilio guy with all the vigor he could muster: "And how the fuck would you know this?"

The guy didn't look like he took any offense. He just shrugged and said: "The man he owes the money to is my uncle, Federico Nunzio. He is also my godfather." He looked around at his five colleagues and added; "He is godfather to all of us."

The Nunzios? They were as big and scary around the North End as the Marcello Family.

I had to give Jimmy credit for what happened next. It could have been one of his worst moments, but it turned out to be one of his best.

He put his hand on Emilio's shoulder and said: "We have to make this right for Sonny. Yes?"

The guy nodded. The other five were now crowded around us, fully involved. They nodded as well.

"Then tell us where we can find your uncle," Jimmy pleaded with him. "We'll explain what happened. But we have to know where he is..."

The guy just shrugged again and pointed to a restaurant right across Hanover Street from us. It was called Coco's Lounge.

"He's in the back," the guy told us. "Tell him you talked to Emilio..."

They say anyone who says they weren't scared in combat is lying to you.

This wasn't combat, but at the time I thought it was real fucking close. We were going into someone else's war with no weapons, and no idea what was going to happen to us. But I remember thinking at the time, in between bouts of trying not to throw up, that at least we'd get whacked while doing the right thing, at the same time wondering if my parents would appreciate such a sacrifice.

Or maybe I just watched too many movies.

I remember I couldn't feel my legs as we walked like two very pale zombies across Hanover Street and up to Coco's Lounge. Even though it was barely eight in the morning, the door was open. We took deep breaths and walked in. It was dark and smelly. No one was at the cash register, no one was at the bar. We kept walking until we came to a door that had to be to the backroom.

We stopped for a moment. What do we do, just walk in? Good way to get shot. But why were there no button men or goons standing guard out here?

We decided the right thing to do was knock. Jimmy gave it three powerful bangs. I expected Luca Brasi to open the door. Instead, we heard someone yell: "Come in!"

I remember looking at each other baffled and mouthing the words: "'Come in?'"

Again, another brave Jimmy moment, because he grabbed the door and opened it, something I would never have done. And so what if Luca didn't answer? I expected this backroom to look like Corleone Central and that the guy's uncle would be portrayed by our friend, Marlo Brando.

What happened was we walked into a typical, open-suite style office, a little run down. The place was filled with smoke; a handful of unassuming guys were playing poker at a round table in the middle. Two more were sitting on the floor, cutting out parts of the Racing Form. One guy was asleep on a very ratty couch. I didn't know who these people were, a numbers joint, maybe a bookie outfit? But they sure weren't the Corleone Clan—not even close.

There was a desk and a computer at the far end of the room. The guy who sat behind it looked like an accountant, complete with bow tie and suspenders, but he had to be Emilio's uncle. There was no one else who seemed to fit the role.

We walked over to the desk, where Jimmy decided to take the quick and easy route. He explained the fruit stand's pink strong box was short a hundred dollars the night before and he was here to pay it back and apologize, emphasizing that he didn't mean to disrespect anyone.

The guy seemed puzzled at first. "You guys Sonny's guys?"

"We are, yes." Jimmy said.

The guy then yelled at the guy who was asleep on the couch: "Did you count what was in the pink box yet?"

The guy hardly stirred.

"It's in my jacket pocket," he called back. "I'll get to it…"

It reached absurdity at that moment because we both realized after going nuts for the last twelve hours or so, these mooks didn't even know the $100 was missing.

Not sure what else to do, Jimmy peeled off the hundred dollars, respectfully put it on the guy's desk and apologized again, saying: "It wasn't Sonny's fault. It was ours, totally."

The guy seemed almost amused at our honesty. "He let a couple of idiots like you take a 'dime' from him?" He laughed, then added: "I appreciate this, boys. I'll talk with Sonny later, but consider us square. Now if that's all, you can get the fuck out."

He put the bills on top of a stack of other bills in the desk's top drawer. Then he added: "And tell that monkey to stay away from Suffolk Downs. He's just no good with the ponies."

It landed then. Sonny wasn't mafioso; he only pretended to be. He was a gambler, and not a good one. I knew the type because I have relatives with the same disease. Sonny must have owed these guys some kind of a substantial sum to agree to sell fruit that hot summer, and to hire his overlord's relatives right off the boat *and* pay a daily vig.

"We will tell him that," said Jimmy.

We backed out of the room slowly, not quite believing it was over and it had been that…well, simple.

But we were wrong. Because no sooner had we reached the door when a small army of Boston cops suddenly burst in. They were wearing motorcycle helmets and swinging nightsticks, shouting orders for everyone to get down on the floor.

Next thing we knew, Jimmy and I were cuffed along with everyone else in the room and dragged down to a waiting paddy wagon. Jimmy knew better than to tell them he was the son of a cop—that would have to come later. Instead, we were transported to a holding facility on Deer Island in Boston Harbor. Once again, Jimmy and I found ourselves in a jail cell, and this time, moms and pops wouldn't be able to bail us out for twenty-five bucks. We knew we were in serious trouble; we just didn't know exactly what kind.

That came out later in the day. The cops separated us and put me in a small room that looked like an interrogation room. I'd seen at least one of these places before and they were always dismal and dirty. I waited there for what seemed like a long time before the door opened, and an elderly and very somber Black woman walked in. I had no idea who she was.

She introduced herself as my rep from DAS.

My heart sank. She was the last person I wanted to see, and it was clear that she wasn't enjoying the moment, either.

She started off by telling me I probably wasn't going to be charged with any gambling offenses. The bad news was I had still violated my DAS agreement. How? By being in the company of known felons, meaning all the Nunzio crew I'd been arrested with earlier that day.

She concluded: "I don't think you'll be able to stay out of prison this time."

PART 2

Chapter Eight

The Kitty Boys of Block Six

Reporters: After all that, when was the next time you were in contact with Al?

Steve Bruce: It was about six months later. I'd heard about the bust at the Nunzios' numbers room but didn't realize until later that Al and his buddy got caught up in it. What are the chances that you're going to be in the backroom of Coco's when the vice squad makes its one and only raid of the year? But it was just another day for Al.

So, I got this letter from him. That's how I found out he was inside, serving six months for violating that stupid DAS agreement for basically clipping a ride on a cold night out of a bad neighborhood. I would have done the same thing.

Anyway, the letter was 44 pages long, hand-written, on yellow legal paper, front and back. It included drawings, some song lyrics and even a couple poems. Al once told me he felt doomed in this world because he was "a left-handed Italian," and they never got anywhere. Maybe so, but this thing was almost a pleasure to read. His penmanship was superb.

He was at a place called Bedford Junction Correctional Center, in Canton, just south of Boston. It was a sort of hybrid facility. It held overflow prisoners when the local jails were too crowded, and it served as a holding area for more serious offenders waiting for a cell at a real prison or a federal lock-up. They used to call it Limbo because everyone inside felt stuck between here, there and nowhere. But by now that had changed to calling it "The Blow Job" or just the BJ for short.

Al described just about every moment he'd spent inside—and he'd barely been there a month when the letter arrived at my precinct. But as we've learned, he's not a bad storyteller and he has a real eye for detail.

His bus left the Charles Street Jail at five on a Sunday morning, arriving at the BJ's receiving center about 30 minutes later. Al told me he was the only white guy on the bus. He went through the usual process of becoming incarcerated. Getting his orange jumpsuit, a sheet, a blanket, one small bar of soap and a small tube of toothpaste. After that, dozens of documents had to be signed and a battery of mugshots taken.

Then came time for the cavity search.

For many first timers, this was when the reality of going to jail finally hit home—and Al said he was no different. A cavity search was everything the name implied. They had to look up your ass to make sure you weren't smuggling anything in. It always sounded unlikely and painful to me, but there were some real pirates out there that could bring in anything from a bag of cocaine to a small pistol.

This was when the BJ's corrections officers made their first appearance; in this case, there were eight of them. Their processing done, the COs had the 22 occupants of the bus line up, turn about face and drop their pants. Al told me he'd been standing right next to a guy he described as bigger than Shaq and twice as scary looking. Little did he know he was also an incredible ventriloquist. When it came time to search his cavity, Al said the big guy manipulated his butt cheeks and in a very deep voice, asked the probing CO: "Excuse me sir, have we met?"

Four COs jumped on the guy immediately. Al said they beat the man "like they were robots." He said it was obvious they'd done it so many times before it was like they were on cruise control.

The rest of the new inmates were ordered to get on the floor, face down, hands behind their heads, pants still down. Al and the others complied and were witness to the big guy fighting off now all eight COs—and laughing about it. In between getting hit with their batons, the prisoner was yelling at them in a spot-on British accent that he was looking forward to eating all their livers someday.

Then the CO's sergeant at arms arrived on the scene. He was essentially the facility's top cop and as Al would learn, a complete asshole. He ran into the holding area, his baton high above his head, obvious he was just dying to crack someone. He had unfortunate timing though, as the giant prisoner had broken free from the other COs just long enough to deliver a massive kick to the sergeant's stomach. This caused the top cop to vomit all over himself, the floor and the guards still wrestling the big guy.

A half dozen workers from the prison's electrical plant were ordered to the scene and only by sheer numbers were they able to finally subdue the prisoner. Cuffed and shackled, he was still laughing as they led him away, imitating Porky Pig, most of the captors displaying various amounts of vomit, blood and other bodily fluids on their persons.

Al said it took another twenty minutes to restore order. By the time the orientation was back on track, the only employee left to continue was the prison's assistant psychologist—and she fainted at the first sight of blood.

The first two weeks of Al's incarceration featured interminable boredom broken only by the occasional "dinner and a show." That meant a fistfight between inmates during chow.

He told me he couldn't believe how noisy the place was, day and night. Clearly some of the prisoners just never went to sleep, spending the early morning hours crying out to each other in catcalls. Al explained that catcalls meant something a little different at the BJ. There was a group of inmates everyone called the Kitty Boys, a dozen or so individuals who were transitioning, transitioned, drag queens and/or gay. They were known to snort instant coffee and then stay up all night meowing to each other.

Al said he learned the rules quickly. Avoid looking anyone in the eye. Never shake hands, always fist bump. Never be nice to the guards. Always wear slippers in the shower. Never get caught up in someone else's business, and absolutely never, ever, take something that's not yours. Keep your word, keep your mouth shut and count down the days.

But the citizens of Massachusetts have always loved their prisoners, or at least they did back then. Al reported that the BJ had an enormous library, second in size only to its enormous work-out facility. Prisoners were offered courses in everything from culinary skills to metaphysics to screenwriting. If there was an incarceration facility that gave inmates a legitimate fresh start, the BJ was at the top of the list.

As I read his letter, I started feeling bad for Al and his predicament. I know from being in LEO that it's best to do prison as an invisible man. Do not call attention to yourself and always stay below the radar. Above all, you don't want to be the funny guy. That's the high-speed passing lane on the road to getting beaten, stabbed, or worse.

Reporters: So, why the sympathy at that point?

Steve Bruce: I had gotten to know Al's family a bit. They're really nice people. And through my interactions with them and him, and especially through this letter, I feel I have gotten to know Al himself in a way. And I knew two things: It would be very hard for Al not to be the funny man. And it would be just about impossible for him to become invisible.

Right around page ten of the letter he told me he'd been assigned to kitchen duties.

As the new fish, his one and only job was taking out the trash. The BJ's cooks made three meals a day for 1,500 inmates and guards. This meant a never-ending flow of white plastic bags full of garbage. They had to be taken to the facility's burn house, right behind the chow hall.

Al said on his first shift, he took out 100 bags of garbage, and that was before lunch. It totaled 203 for the day. He said it wasn't back-breaking work, but it was repetitive and right in line with the institutionalized boredom of the place.

That all changed his third morning working in the kitchens. An inmate he'd never seen before walked up to him and gave him a full trash bag. Al turned to put it on top of his always growing pile of trash bags to go, when the guy stopped him and said: "No—this is for the blocko...hide it someplace warm."

Al looked in the bag and said it contained about a dozen rotten apples, lots of mushy molding bread, crumbled up pieces of cookies, candy bars and what looked like handfuls of grape jelly. Basically, garbage.

Al asked the guy, why hide it? I'll just throw it out. But at that point, Al said he realized the inmate was holding something close to his stomach. It was a severely sharpened yellow Number 2 pencil, considered a deadly weapon inside the BJ.

"Just hide it someplace warm, fish," he told Al again. "That's mando from Torpedo Six."

Then the guy disappeared.

Al explained he was perplexed by what happened. Why would an inmate he didn't know threaten to stab him if he didn't hide a bag of rotting garbage in a warm spot? He'd been warned that many inmates at the BJ were on brake fluid, slang for psychiatric medications. They were best avoided, especially if they're displaying shivs and threatening people they don't know.

He didn't mention the incident to anyone. He hid the bag behind one of the bread ovens and the one and only time he checked it, a day later, it looked and smelled putrid.

He was ending his Friday shift, lugging out a final couple dozen garbage bags before he could call it quits. Just as he was about to report out with the kitchen CO, he found the facility's sergeant at arms waiting for him near the bread ovens.

This guy lived up to his reputation as the prison's biggest asshole, crooked as hell and always quick to write you up. Al had no idea what he wanted with him and so surprised the crap out of him by asking the location of the bag of rotting garbage. Al admitted he was shaking a little as he directed this baboon to the bag hidden behind the bread oven. But they both had to fall back when they got within a few feet of it. The smell was that bad.

The guy told Al to grab the bag and to follow him. Al reminded me that he used to pick up stiffs for a living and had seen some pretty ugly situations complete with some pretty ugly smells.

But he said nothing compared to this.

He was totally befuddled—his word—at what the top CO wanted with him and the soggy, smelly bag of trash. They walked in silence over to the 6 Block, two away from Al's neighborhood.

They opened the block main door and that's when Al learned what a blocko was.

Each block had a head inmate—called torpedoes—the leader of the gang, so to speak. Number's 6's torpedo was nicknamed Hedgehog and he was finally catching the chain, as in getting out, and the block was having a going away party, a blocko. The gathering was to be held in the TV room and the guards had already been told by the top CO not to be hard asses.

And the bag of rotting garbage? It contained the essential makings of a prison moonshine called pruno. Fermented bread, fermented fruit, crushed sugar cookies, jelly and a little mouth wash, stomp it, drain it and voila! Pruno… The prison wine looked, smelled and tasted like something better off going down the drain. But it provided a strong buzz.

The inmates in 6 Block greeted Al like a hero when he arrived with the precious bag. Two men took it from him and quickly disappeared into one of the cells to complete the final product. The 6's TV room had been laid out and ready for the party. Someone had liberated some beach chairs. One table held lots of wham-whams (cookies) and zoom-zooms (candy). They even had a big screen color TV with a stack of porn videos waiting nearby.

Al told me he couldn't help but want to stay, if just for the wham-whams. Then, just as one of the inmates started to lead him out, they heard a collective groan from others in the TV room. The VCR wasn't working. Al immediately piped up and said he'd been a VCR mechanic on the outside and he could fix the cranky machine. It was a total lie, of course, but that didn't bother Al.

It took him less than thirty seconds to diagnose the problem. A switch in the back had been inadvertently moved from TV to cable. Al switched it back and the TV came to life.

He got a boisterous round of applause from the grateful partygoers. When the inmate who'd been leading him out reappeared, Al simply asked him: "Do you want me to stay? It might happen again…"

The inmate looked at the CO sergeant who just shrugged. "I don't know how to fix the damn thing if it goes out again, do you?"

After a few moments of thought, the inmate told Al: "Okay...just don't make an asshole of yourself."

There were 21 inmates in Block 6 and Al reported that within an hour everyone was buzzed on pruno, including him.

He emphasized that it tasted worse than it smelled but it did the job in spades. After just a handful of dixie cups of the stuff, he said he hadn't been that incapacitated since the Salisbury Beach Hash Brownie incident.

The party turned into a haze of porno movies, spilled pruno and jamming wham-whams. His memory was foggy on most of what happened, but he told me there were a few things that were impossible to forget.

After a raucous discussion about which movie to watch first, the winner was "Blood on the Playground," a half porn, half slasher movie. In one scene a girl gets her throat cut in a particularly slow and gruesome manner. When it was over, Al remembered one of the inmates turned to him and said: "You know, there's a better way of doing that..."

Al figures he must have excused himself after that, because he wandered into the open cell where the pruno had been made. It smelled worse than the juice itself. Then he said he came upon a group of inmates, huddled in one corner of another open cell, inexplicably licking what looked to be children's drawings. When they turned to look at him, bare phantoms inside of dark shadows, Al saw they all had the droops. Their eyes, their lips, their entire faces, visibly drooping, their pupils bare pinpoints in a sea of bloodshot and white.

Heroin...

But how? Prisoners were searched frequently. Visitors are also thoroughly searched. The guards were all dishonest, but Al just didn't see them letting heroin through. So, how were the prisoners getting it? And where did the kids' drawings come in?

One of the coffee-snorting Kitty Boys sidled up to him, and filled him in.

There were two kinds of conjugal visits at the BF. A boneyard visit was when a wife or girlfriend visited an inmate for sexual relations. The second kind of conjugal visit was the FamBam, a visit that included the entire family.

The Kitty explained that during FamBams, certain inmates would get the drawings from their kids and then protect them like they were gold. Why? Because the "paint" on the drawings wasn't paint at all; it was a combination of baking powder, food dye and methanol, a synthetic form of heroin that was used in some recovery programs. By simply licking the colors off the drawings the prisoners got a heroin-like buzz for hours. (Al later told me that another time, another day, during a trip to the infirmary to get a band-aid, he saw a different kind of licking going on. Meth addicts, in custody and going through withdrawals so badly they were sucking on each other's wounds, hoping to extract some of the meth from their compatriots' blood stream.)

The blocko was in full swing by eight o'clock. The porn movies were running, another jug of pruno was going around and the inmates were gobbling down the cookies and Tootsie Rolls.

Suddenly the block door opened, and a dozen men were let in by a CO. The TV room went quiet. These people hadn't been invited to the party. This was a crash, courtesy of some paid-off guard.

The ringleader was a huge guy, shaven head, and tats everywhere. His nickname was Butterball because he had a huge rear end. Despite his calculated scary appearance, he was a hedge fund guy doing five years for wire fraud. He'd been parked at the BJ for nearly half of it now, waiting to be transferred to a federal prison.

The 6 Block's torpedo, Hedgehog, was also in for bank fraud. But he was a completely different kind of animal. So short he was almost lost in his orange jumpsuit, he looked more like a college professor than a Wall Street crook. He was doing just two years and had been tipped off early that he might do it all at the BJ—a tip that proved true. Now he was just days away from getting out for good.

Butterball and Hedgehog were briefly business partners—now they were arch enemies. And as far as prison beefs went, theirs was a good one.

Lots of gambling went on inside the BJ. Cards, dominoes, basketball—even tic-tac-toe. Instead of money, the winnings would include things from the commissary like wham-whams and zoom-zooms.

But the top currency inside the facility were cigarettes; "bats" in the lingo. Tobacco was not sold legally on the inside, but Butterball had been working a scam to sell cigarettes *illegally* to his fellow prisoners. He had someone on the outside send him contraband by tying it to heavy gauge deer-hunting arrows and shooting them over the BJ's twenty-foot wall. Light weight burner phones, dozens of illegal pills, even small bags of cocaine had been airlifted into the BJ this way. They were called bindles.

The deal was Butterball would have the bindles shot in and Hedgehog would sell the stuff to the prison population in return for cigarettes, which they would sell back to the inmates and then split the profits. But because Butterball was such a tool, almost immediately he began accusing Hedgehog of stealing from him—one hundred bats to be precise. The beef was born.

After weeks of threats and counter-threats and the possibility of an all-out block war, someone suggested they settle their dispute by playing a game of chess. Al mentioned that even though the BJ's huge library was hardly used, he was surprised how many of the prison population knew how to play chess. There were frequent tournaments, and they were always heavily bet on because it was widely believed that a chess game could not be fixed.

A large crowd witnessed that first Butterball-Hedgehog game. Hedgehog won in a breeze, David beating a fat-ass Goliath on just ten moves. But once again, Butterball's d-bag genes burst forth, claiming among other things that the little guy's chess pieces, carved out of soap, were intentionally too small and that the cell where the match was held was intentionally too dark.

Neither claim made sense, but Butterball's flunkies spread the fake news around anyway. By the next day, the entire jail had heard that Hedgehog was a cheat.

Al knew little of this when he found himself at the blocko. He also admitted he'd feared for his life for a few moments because it looked like a serious fight was going to break out between Butterball's guys and the 6 Block crew—and he'd be caught in the middle of it.

As it happened, Butterball walked right up to Hedgehog, who was sitting next to the TV and got in his grill. A lot of Block Six guys were standing behind Hedgehog, backing him up, but Butterball and his crew were undaunted. Butterball told him he'd heard the 'Hog was getting an early release. If that was so, he demanded the 100 bats he owed him…or else.

Now here they were, ready to go to war. With no guards around, the weapons came out. Butterball had a shaved-down metal spoon; Hedgehog had a can of tuna wrapped in a sock. Al told me he watched it all from across the room, desperately not wanting to get into someone else's Kool-Aid. But it was clear that Butterball wanted to put the clutch on Hedgehog, that is, goad him into a fight, get him busted by the COs which would then cancel his imminent release because he'd be under disciplinary watch. Getting another Walk Date might not happen for weeks or even months.

Despite this, Al said he could see Hedgehog was about to lose his cool. He looked like a kid who'd been bullied on the playground too many times and finally had enough. His fists were balled, his jaw was out, tuna can and sock waiting to lay into the giant of a man, which was exactly what the Butterball wanted.

Al said he would never know why he did it, other than he was severely buzzed on pruno, but he suddenly found himself leaping across the room and coming in between the two men.

"Settle it with another chess game," he told them, suddenly the center of attention. "Neutral site, plenty of light, one that can't be fixed…"

As Al tells it, Butterball grabbed him and was about to stab him, when one of 'Ball's lieutenants intervened.

"Listen to him," this man said. "It might be the only way you'll ever get your bats."

Al said Butterball was now about an inch from his face and that he smelled like medicine, maybe brake fluid.

Finally, he snarled at Al: "OK. Neutral site? Plenty of light? Set it up, fish. You're not going anywhere anytime soon. You'll fuck this up and when you do, I can take my time giving you a shave…"

Chapter Nine

The Hippopotamus Fluid Defense

Reporters: What happened next?

Steve Bruce: Al wrote that he wasn't sure he was in for a beating until the next morning when he ran into one of the 6 Block guys at chow.

The guy filled in some of the memory blanks, a common side effect of drinking pruno. In Al's mind, he'd prevented a brawl during which he might have gotten sliced. To everyone else, he'd promised the jail's most fucked-up torpedo something that was impossible to deliver, thus the beating-in-waiting.

The problem was the design of the Bedford Junction facility. It was a circular building, divided into nine different blocks. Just like at any prison, tradition dictated that each block defend its turf, fiercely if necessary. But this idea was taken to the nth degree at the BJ. There were lines painted down the middle of the kitchen, the latrines, the showers and running throughout the mess hall, the library and the gym, unofficially marking everyone's neighborhoods, right down to the last square inch, and that was no exaggeration. To be caught trespassing might not get you stabbed right away, but you better have a good reason for being where you weren't supposed to be.

The point that began to dawn on Al was, there might not be any neutral place inside the BJ. Even the parking lots had been divided up. With no place considered non-aligned, in the minds of many, Al was so dumb, he deserved to get beat.

Reporters: And isn't it virtually impossible to avoid a beating in prison? The place is so relatively small eventually you're going to run into your attacker, right?

Steve Bruce: That's correct. People think the guards are around all the time, but they're not. And sometimes the ones who are might be on the take from some other cellblock and then you have a very bad, and yes, almost inevitable situation if the person planning the beat-down is committed enough.

But Al managed to avoid it—or at least postpone it—because he remembered one crucial thing. On his first day at the BJ, he'd noticed the receiving area had a tiled floor. While waiting for the COs to subdue the man who made his ass talk British, Al realized, from a floor level, that the tile layout in the middle of this room matched that of a huge chess board. Sixty-four squares, half dirty white, the others black. He'd wondered at the time if this had been intentional.

Al began to recount how many advantages this place had to host the chess match and to save him from getting a beatdown. The giant tile chess board was perfect to debunk anything being too small. There was a steel walkway one flight up where the COs could easily watch over a large crowd. And unlike the first Hedgehog-Butterball clash, which was held on a bunk in a cramped cell, the receiving area was so well-lit, it would be impossible to fix a chess match by "low-lighting."

Best of all, it solved the whole turf question. The receiving area was also the prison's discharge point, that place where people getting out signed a few documents, got their valuables back and were turned loose, free to go. Because of all this coming and going, it was never really considered to be part of the prison. It had always been unclaimed territory.

The solution to the problem? Play the Second Hedgehog-Butterball match here.

Al told his plan to Hedgehog and one of Hedgehog's emissaries brought the idea to Butterball. When word came back that Butterball had agreed, Hedgehog indicated he would take it from there.

Al heard nothing about it for three days. Finally, Hedgehog sought him out at late chow and told him everything was set. They'd play the match in the receiving area. The COs knew what was up. For a few bucks, the CO sergeant had convinced the Warden that the chess game would be a good way to cool off tensions inside the jail. The warden gave his okay.

Things moved fast after that. One of the Kitty Boys used his collection of brightly colored pieces of chalk to draw an impressive border around the massive chess board. It featured stars and planets and hills of grass and waving trees, all the things one does not see in jail.

The 6 Block guys laid out the holding facility with folding chairs from the chapel and tables from the commissary. When they were through, it looked like a boxing ring with a big chess board in the middle. Other tables nearby held bowls of wham-whams and zoom-zooms with signs warning two per inmate. By agreement, no pruno was involved, but the Kitty Boys had gotten ahold of a few cases of Zolt Cola, a highly caffeinated pop drink that, while not making you high or cranked-out, had enough kick that everyone was guaranteed to be highly attentive throughout the match.

Gambling was second only to eating at the BJ. The chess game was being bet everywhere and by everybody in the facility including, the grapevine said, the warden and his hot wife. The smart money had Hedgehog and Butterball at just about even money. When word went around the jail that 'Ball had been studying his chess moves via an on-line course, Hedgehog intentionally leaked a story that he was growing concerned Butterball was taking their second match too seriously.

The chess pieces were empty five-gallon sauce buckets from the kitchen. Half were painted white, the other red. Each player had an assistant. The player would make his decision where to move and then the helper would move the bucket piece as instructed. Such was the gravitas of the bout that the assistants were moving the buckets around an hour before the game began, just to get the feel of it.

Many COs, both off duty and not, were up on the walkway, on hand to see the chess game for the ages. A lot of the prison's administrative help were on hand, too. But Al might have had the best seat of all. Right at the 50-yard-line, Hedgehog's camp to his right, Butterball's to his left.

The funny thing was, afterwards Al told me he didn't know how to play chess, didn't have a clue how it went.

So, when the game finally started, he had absolutely no idea what was going on.

Hedgehog arrived on time, his body crew surrounding him, serious but unintrusive. They received a warm reception. But knowing well his acute diva complex, everyone expected Butterball to make a grand entrance—and he did not disappoint.

He burst into the big room, a white bathrobe thrown around him, his crew noisily pushing inmates aside to make way for the fat ass king. This resulted in a rain of boos. Butterball started screaming back at the crowd, claiming he was taking the names of anyone he saw booing him. The boos became twice as loud. Butterball challenged several inmates to fight him then and there—clearly he'd been watching too much WWF. His gang finally pulled him away from the hecklers and into the ring.

Now, a hush came over the crowd. The two combatants met in the center of the huge chess board, nose to clavicle. Al said it was like a prize fight—the tension, the excitement, the crowd. The betting in the stands reached peak ferocity. Everything was up for currency—fake pot, real coke, fake heroin, real zoom-zooms. But in the end, it was all about the bats. Betting ten bats was considered ballsy. Betting twenty would be considered insanity, until one was reminded this whole thing was about a hundred bats. A literal fortune.

The game began. With the players now standing at either end of the huge board and calling out to their flunkies holding the buckets, Al thought the opening moves were intentionally simple, like in checkers. But the prisoners' gallery disagreed. They followed each move like it was a pitch in the last inning in the seventh game of the World Series, complete with gasps and frantic post-move discussions. Al said he was floored. In a place where a lot of people were borderline illiterate, everyone seemed to be experts in chess. Except him.

Certain the match would last hours, many in the crowd brought lunches. Sandwiches, bags of chips, cans of Zolt; they settled in for what everyone thought was going to a long time.

But they were wrong.

As Al later found out, after those first few moves, Hedgehog began hitting Butterball with a series of famous if obscure chess strategies. One was called the Monkey's Bum. The way Hedgehog had his assistant running all over the board was almost comical, leaving Butterball completely stumped. Then Hedgehog employed something called the Frankenstein Variation. It managed to surround almost all of Butterball's force in three lightning moves.

So suddenly on his heels, the 'Ball tried to roar back, attempting to break out of the trap. But the on-line courses failed him, and he made two bonehead excuse-me moves that did nothing but make him look foolish. Smelling blood, Hedgehog employed the Hippopotamus Fluid Defense, essentially trapping 'Ball once again, just in a different place on the board.

Al said, even having no idea what was going on, it was apparent less than a minute into the match that Butterball was totally baffled. The cracks started to show quickly. When the 'Ball slapped his assistant for not moving his bucket fast enough, Hedgehog delivered the knock-out blow. It was an almost-ancient move known as The Capablanca Switch.

And that's all it took. Check and mate, 1:51 into the match.

The audience was stunned. They'd just got there! But once they realized what happened, the applause was riotous. Butterball's face turned cherry red. Not only had he lost, but he'd been wildly outsmarted in the process—and everyone knew it.

He and his men charged across the chess board towards the Hedgehogs; suddenly the situation went DEFCON1 and looked like it would go full nuclear. Meeting the assault at about the halfway spot on the board, both gangs were ready to knuckle up when someone smartly killed all the lights. There was a lot of pushing and shoving in the dark until the COs finally got down from the walkway and broke up the confrontation.

Once the lights were restored, Butterball and his crew were escorted from the receiving area, yelling death threats over their shoulders in Hedgehog's direction.

But it didn't make any difference.

Hedgehog called in one last favor from someone and got out even earlier than scheduled. Before anyone knew it, he was gone, not an hour after he'd won the match.

The 6 Block guys were devastated. The little man had been a great torpedo, and no one knew what to do now that he was gone. There was talk of breaking up the block, something the administration did on occasion anyway. Instead, they took Hedgehog's advice from beyond the grave and went looking for another torpedo, someone to slot in and take over, like nothing had happened.

They approached Al the next day and asked if he'd take the position. Al being Al, immediately said yes. An hour later, he found the contents of his cell taken from 3 Block to 6 Block, which was suddenly his little kingdom.

Page 22…

That's where in his very long letter Al explained he'd become a top dog at the BJ. True, it had a great gymnasium and a gigantic library, but it was still a jail, and now Al had attained the high status of Torpedo. Believe me, I was as surprised as I'm sure you are right now. But that was Al Ferrari. Impossible to be invisible.

He found himself in a position he'd never experienced before. He'd never been a boss, a supervisor, or a ringleader. Now he was all three. And he'd inherited a handful of second lieutenants that, while not overtly kissing his ass, were glad to do anything he needed.

He also found himself in consultations with other torpedoes from the other blocks. No one was ever overly nice to each other, but all agreed communication was key, because miscommunication could result in BB filler, as in someone going into a body bag for the long ride out.

There was inevitable tension with Butterball's 5 Block guys, though. They'd never considered splitting up, deciding instead to stick by their man. Being the pompous clown that he was, Butterball sent his flunkies throughout the facility, making it known he had irrefutable proof Hedgehog fixed the second match, just like the first—and then ran away when he was caught. Quoting the 'Ball, "The little rat screwed all of us out of a hundred bats."

Not so subtle were the warnings that made it back to Al that Butterball was planning his revenge on 6 Block, and as the new torpedo, he should watch his back—and frankly the rest of his body too.

To his credit, Al didn't freak out. But he took the gossip seriously. He knew Butterball would try to goad him into a fight, to throw the first punch. This way the fat ass could seriously injure him, call it self-defense and the screws would have to go along with it.

So, Al was not surprised a few nights later when he was approached by the CO sergeant and handed a message from Butterball. It was printed neatly on half of a paper plate. It read: "Don't listen to the noise. Let's call a truce and revive the business me and Hedgehog had."

The sergeant added, "The Ball would like to meet by the south wall during exercise tomorrow morning and bump fists on his idea."

Al was no fool—the last thing he wanted was to face the 'Ball alone. But he also knew if he didn't meet Mrs. Butterass, the other guys in the 6 Block would pay the price, not just from the 5 Block guys, but around the entire facility. Their torpedo was a pussy and they were stupid to put him in charge.

So, the next day at the appointed time, Al walked over to the south wall. He said he was extremely nervous, but who could blame him? His only real hope was that not all the COs had been paid off and with a few still around, 'Ball couldn't stab him. But even he knew this was a very long shot.

Al had a weapon, but it was a crude one. It was called a crapper. Three toilet handles taped together at the bottom and held between the individual fingers, basically DIY brass knuckles. It was better than trying to hit someone with a bare fist, but not much more. Al said it felt like bringing a squirt gun to a gunfight.

Butterball was already there when he reached the south wall, looking as obese as ever. As Al approached, he said he became aware that 'Ball was holding his famous shorn-off spoon; he could see the sun glinting off its razor edge.

Al stopped and looked around to find his worst fear come true: all the COs had disappeared—except one. The sergeant. He was looking down at them from the South Tower. But as soon as the 'Ball showed his weapon, the sergeant turned his back on the whole thing, and vanished as well.

Butterball took a step towards Al. He asked him just how dumb he was. Why would he want to bring in another Hedgehog when he, the 'Ball, could make all the money and bats himself?

Al barely heard him. He gripped the crapper in his pocket, knowing his only chance was to get close as possible to the giant and if he attacked, then take the blow and then swing back, and hope if he survived, the screws would see it as self-defense on his part and not the other way around.

Either way, it was a bad position to be in; so much so, Al said he tensed up, every muscle coiled, but unable to move. Seeing this, Butterball laughed and said: "That's okay. Just stand there and make it easy for me…"

He lunged forward to stab Al in the chest, but Al suddenly came alive and avoided the blow. Butterball laughed manically. "Oh good, let's make it a game," he said.

Another lunge, this one so close, it tore the front of Al's jumpsuit. Al stumbled back but managed to pull out his weapon. "Don't get caught with that," Butterball told him with another evil grin. "You'll wind up in solitary…"

He came at Al a third time, this one for the kill, but… before Al could even react with the crapper, Butterball suddenly froze in place, as if paralyzed. The shaved spoon fell from his hand; his face went white. He looked down at Al, not with hate in his eyes, but with astonishment.

He mouthed the words, "What's happened to me…"

Then he fell over right next to Al, hitting face-first on the concrete, breaking his nose, his right cheek, his right suborbital bone and his jaw, losing six teeth and knocking himself out cold.

Sticking out of his rear end was a heavy gauge deer-hunting arrow with a bindle of cocaine and ten cell phone batteries attached.

Chapter Ten

How to Turn a Celica into a Rolls Royce

Reporters: Al had some family connections with other LEOs, correct?

Steve Bruce: Yes, he had a cousin who was a Mass. Registry cop.

Reporters: And this connection led to Al getting, shall we say, a change in location?

Steve Bruce: It didn't hurt. I've met the guy. His name is Bobby Cantina and he's okay. The Registry of Motor Vehicles used to have their own cops. They'd solve automotive crimes, stolen cars, stolen inspection stickers, stuff like that. They were usually tough motherfuckers and even other cops knew not to screw with them. It's just one of the many ironies in Al's life. He had a talent for boosting cars and his cousin's job was to stop guys like him.

Al told me Cousin Bobby came to visit him at the BJ shortly after the Butterball episode. It turned out that after 007 Fat-Ass recovered from his injuries, he was finally launched on his long-awaited trip to Federal prison to serve out the rest of his sentence and no doubt make hell for someone else farther up the river.

Bobby brought Al some car magazines, zoom-zooms and, most valuable: five books of postage stamps. Stamps were the second highest-level currency in the joint, next to bats. In so many ways, they are your connection to the outside world.

At some point the conversation turned to how brilliant the people at the Massachusetts Registry had become. Bobby bragged that in the past five years, the Registry had taken down fifty percent more motor vehicle criminals than in the previous twenty years combined, all thanks to the Registry's Computer-Assisted Bureau, which Bobby now ran.

"Every little last thing is on the computer," he told Al. "There's just no way anyone can get away with anything, anymore…"

Al said he laughed so loud, the CO told him to calm down.

"You guys are idiots," he supposedly told his cousin. "You've been missing one of the biggest scams ever—and all thanks to your crappy computer systems."

Cousin Bobby was pissed but also perversely intrigued. He told Al to spill.

Al claimed about two years before, a gang from Charlestown had figured out a fool-proof way of committing serious insurance fraud, one of Al's favorite sports. They called themselves the Shady Brothers Crew. They weren't masterminds, but they didn't have to be. They'd simply found a loophole in how the Registry handled titles from cars previously registered in Massachusetts but now registered somewhere else.

Their scheme had five steps: Step one: buy a shit-box car, get the title, and register the car in Mass. Step two: move the car to Florida. Step three: use a forged title to re-register the car in Florida, (which requires only seeing the title document and not the car itself), but do it as something super-expensive, like a Rolls-Royce. Step four: Insure it, wait a month, then report it stolen. Step five: collect the Rolls Royce-sized insurance settlement.

While Florida would eventually mail the forged title back to Mass, there was no system in place to cross-reference it with the Registry's vaunted computer-driven internal data base. In other words, there was nothing to indicate a ten-year-old Celica had suddenly turned into a brand-new Rolls Silver Shadow. Any titles that came in this way were physically destroyed by a shredding company hired by the Registry.

Pretty simple really.

But how did Al know all this? Because he knew the Shady Brothers Crew—and they were hardly a gang. They were in fact the three brothers from Chelsea who served as the poppers at Palumbo Printing. These were the low-level guys who would shlep rolls of paper to the printer and then shlep them back when they were done.

But every few weeks, they would stay after hours and use the biggest, most modern printing press … to create the blank Registry titles.

Everyone working there knew the brothers were up to no good, but because old man Palumbo was such a prick, the word around the building was look the other way. But… one of the brothers ripped Al off once. He stole his meatball sub out of the microwave. So, being Sicilian, Al always dreamed of a way to jam this guy up. His chat with Cousin Bobby gave him that chance.

Not that Cousin Bobby believed any of it at first. Cutting his visit short, he threw Al his magazines, stamps and cookies and left.

But a few days later, Al got a message he was wanted in the Warden's conference room. He arrived to find six Registry big shots waiting for him, all decked out in their uniforms and medals. There were curt introductions, then another guy walked in, he in a suit coat and tie, and he was introduced to Al as *his* attorney. When Al asked why he would need an attorney, they explained while the meeting was off the record, the lawyer was there so Al wouldn't incriminate himself.

They told him to repeat to them everything he'd told his cousin, this time slowly and clearly. Al knew they were skeptical any such scam existed. But he explained how easy it was to take the codes off shit-box car titles and flawlessly print them onto the forged titles. With the equipment in a modern graphics shop, he said, just about anyone could do it.

They gave him a dummy car title and asked him to demonstrate as best he could. Al immediately took the piece of paper and cut out where the present title number was located. Making a perfect square, he wrote a fake number on a blank piece of paper, then put it behind this window and pretended to take a photograph of it.

"I'm pretty sure you guys wouldn't notice the difference unless you were really looking for it," he told them that day. "But I can guarantee some RMV worker in Florida will miss it every time."

Al recalled the half dozen big shots looked at him with identical pale faces. The incarcerated cousin/car thief/insurance fraudster had just proved their beloved Computer-Assisted Bureau had a gaping hole in it.

Starting the following day, any old titles returned to Massachusetts were no longer destroyed. They were sent instead to Cousin Bobby, who went through each one, entering them in the Registry's data system by hand. Within a week, he found out the Shady Brothers Crew had used the scheme to collect a payout on a high-end BMW F5 sports car just a few days before.

It took another week to gather the evidence, but one early Chelsea morning the Registry cops swooped down on the Shady Brothers and arrested all three on charges of grand larceny and insurance fraud. Around the same time, someone high up in the Registry got a judge to grant Al an extended furlough from the BJ, a reward for his help in busting the SBC.

With the flick of a pen, Al was suddenly a free man.

It was a Friday night when he found out.

He'd finished his last shift working in the kitchens and had helped draw them down. He was one of the last ones out, having cleared the vast galley of dozens of smelly, leaky and totally gross garbage bags. Although he was now well-known inside the jail, his elevated status did nothing to get him out of working his shitty day job.

But as soon as he returned to his cell, he found a CO waiting for him. He told Al to pack his things and be ready to leave the BJ for good in exactly one hour. When Al asked him why, the CO just walked away.

Al said he felt like he was in a dream. He couldn't believe what was happening, certain there had been a colossal fuck up somehow. But he did as told, and barely had time to wish his jail buds goodbye. He knew he'd never see them again. That was the code. Friendships end at the gate. It was easier to start a new life that way.

He was rushed through the discharge process and signed for his valuables. Only then was he told in a prepared statement read by the discharge point guard that he was getting sprung for helping the Registry with a matter of great importance.

He was escorted to the front gate. Outside, his cousin Bobby was waiting in his blue Registry cruiser, engine roaring, blue lights spinning madly, everything but the siren.

Quite the Welcome Back, Al thought.

But then he saw his cousin motioning frantically for him to get in the car. That's when Al knew something else was up. He climbed into the front seat and his cousin said to him: "I'm sorry Al—I just got a really bad call. One of your parents had a heart attack and died about an hour ago." Al said he felt like he'd been hit in the head with a hammer, something that had happened to him for real at least twice before. But Cousin Bobby had even more bad news. "The problem is my station doesn't know which one it was," he said. "That's the only info I could get through my office which they got from the Everett PD."

Al said he immediately slumped low in the cruiser's front seat. A cosmic kick in the balls, that's how he saw it. He's a free man for exactly sixty seconds before he learns one of his parents was gone.

Bobby was very upset that he couldn't get the identity of the deceased parent, screaming over the radio, trying his best but to no avail.

But Al didn't even have to think about it.

He knew which one it was.

Chapter Eleven

A Ghost in the Family

Reporters: Can you tell us about that night? What was going through your mind?

Al: Like anyone put in that position, I was thinking about my parents and especially my mother. You know, as a kid, I didn't realize how good a mother she was until it was too late. She gave everything to me and my brothers and how did I repay her? By going to jail.

She never visited me at the BJ. She wrote me every day, though. Only later did I find out that several times she made it as far as the parking lot, but she just couldn't come in. She couldn't stand to see her son in jail. But a letter came every day and believe me, things like that work wonders when you're locked up. On top of everything else, she'd had health problems, and me being incarcerated sure didn't help that situation. I promised myself that when I got out, I'd treat her like a queen and somehow try to pay her back for all she'd done for me and for sticking by me.

Now I was sure that chance was gone...

These were the things I was thinking about as we raced up Interstate 95 and then onto Route 1, heading towards Everett. Full siren, lights swirling and topping 110 M.P.H. I learned one thing: when people see a Registry car with lights flashing behind them, they move over so quickly it's like we were racing at Monte Carlo. But the siren was so noisy we really couldn't talk.

My cousin kept trying to get more information from the Everett PD, but no one had anything more to report except one parent had died about an hour before.

It didn't matter, though.

I knew it was my mother.

We reached Barman's Court inside an hour; amazing time, really.

The entire dead-end was packed with cars, some double parked. My Italian relatives, showing up in droves, all of them carrying a covered dish or an iced coffee cake. But there was also another car there, parked right in front of the house, one that looked all too familiar. It was a hearse from one of the funeral homes Johnny O'Neil had been forced to sell, though at a pretty-good profit. I learned later that Johnny paid for everything that came our way in the next few days. He picked up all the funeral and burial expenses, he even paid the priest. Johnny was a solid guy and stuff like that went a long way in Everett. I'll never forget what he did for us during that really bad time.

Barman's Court was so crowded, my cousin Bobby had to let me out in front and then find a place to park his cruiser. Every light in our house was on and I could see dozens of people already milling around inside.

I hurried around to the back door—and ran into someone coming out the other way.

It was my mother.

We both startled each other. I thought I was seeing a ghost. Then she hugged me and started to cry.

"It's your father, Al," she said. "He's gone…"

My dad? Youngest of nine kids born to an immigrant couple from Palermo. Learned English at Catholic school, lived in the North End. Enlisted in the Army the day after Pearl Harbor, got married, moved to

East Boston, had two kids, then moved to Everett, to Barman's Court. They had kid number three there, and that was me.

My dad worked his ass off. He managed a huge parking garage in downtown Boston, and it was a 24/7 job. Sometimes we wouldn't see him for a couple days, like during blizzards. But he was a great guy. Never raised a hand to his kids, never raised his voice to my mother. We never went hungry, and we were always warm at night.

I went inside, mingled with the family until I managed to see them all, kiss them all, thank them all, hug them all—and then say good night.

I hadn't been in my old room for almost a year. Nothing had changed. All my posters were still on the wall, all my porn books, I'm sure, still in the air vent. My mother had refused to change anything. She wanted to keep it that way for when I was finally free and could sleep on clean sheets again.

I went to bed and was in dreamland about a minute later.

At some point, the house had cleared out of relatives and mourners. I woke up in the middle of the night to the smell of burnt iced coffee cake. I looked out the window to see all the cars were gone off Barman's Court—except one: my father's. His Chevy station wagon was parked in the driveway like it always was, close by the back door.

I was about to turn away and take a leak, when I heard the wagon's rear door slam shut. I would have known that sound anywhere. Shadows from the trees obscured most of the view, but I could see a figure down there as well and they'd definitely closed the clunky rear door.

My first thought was one of my brothers was getting something out of dad's car. But I looked in both their rooms and they were as out of it as I had been just a few moments before.

I went downstairs thinking two things: either one of my relatives was staying over and needed something in dad's wagon—or, almost inconceivable at that moment—someone was breaking into the station wagon and trying to steal it.

As I reached the kitchen, intent on grabbing a carving knife and going outside, I saw the shadow of someone on the other side of the frosted glass coming up to the back door. Very broad shoulders, half-sized fedora tilted back on the head. They were carrying three bags of groceries.

I was absolutely paralyzed. I couldn't move or breathe. The door opened … and a dark figure walked in.

It was my dad.

"Are you going to just stand there or help me?" he asked.

I just stood there. I was in shock, in the dark kitchen. I tried to turn on the light, but it wouldn't work. It looked as if all the streetlights had gone out too.

But I could see my dad clearly. He put the groceries down, then sat at the table and took his hat off and bent the brim back into shape. I'd seen him do the same thing hundreds of times before.

I was finally able to say something. I asked him if he was all right.

He looked at me strangely and replied: "Why wouldn't I be? I feel fine. You don't have to worry about me…"

Then he motioned me over closer to the kitchen table. I stared at him for the longest time. He looked different in a way. Like all the troubles he'd carried around with him all those years were gone. He looked younger, happier. His eyes were full of an inner light.

"You have to remember to take care of your mother," he said, still fiddling with his hat. "I'm leaving that up to you because I know you'll do a good job. Okay?"

"But why do I have to do it?" I asked him. "Because you're okay, there's been some mix up. You're here. You're alive."

He stood up and kind of brushed himself off. "Just do me that favor, will you?" he said. "Look after her. Promise?"

I nodded and told him: "Sure thing. Pop…"

He thought a moment, picked up the three bags of groceries and said, "Come to think of it, I might need these."

Then he went out the back door.

But he left his hat behind; I know this because it was there when I got up the next morning.

The wake was the following night and it was a small mob scene in more ways than one.

Hundreds came, and nearly everyone commented on how beautiful the casket looked. This was also Johnny O'Neil's doing. The casket was a European design, solid mahogany, wide at the shoulders and narrow at the feet, with red wax covering the heads of the screws that held it together.

It was beautiful and Johnny hoped it would make my mother feel better. That was a tough call though, because she'd become majorly withdrawn, especially after she watched the funeral home guys drive away that night.

She hadn't said much to anyone since, just nodding to those offering comfort and condolences, but hardly speaking at all.

We all noticed it. And that just wasn't like my mother.

The next day arrived cold, dark and rainy, typical early March. We got to the funeral home just as they were placing the casket in the back of their best hearse.

I remember the ride to the church seemed to take hours. We finally arrived and I noticed there was a huge set of stairs leading up to the front door—forty-nine in all. The funeral home had told us to have eight pallbearers; now we found out why. The casket had no handles. The idea was to lift it onto our shoulders and hopefully balance it all the way up. But it was very heavy. It took all eight of us plus the drivers just to get the casket out of the hearse and even more volunteers to put it up on our shoulders.

The climb up those forty-nine steps was terrifying, I was just praying the casket wouldn't fall and crack open. But we made it somehow, a slow, but in the end a successful ascent. I couldn't wait to put it down on the rolling cart and finally walk into the church, which also turned out to be gloomy as hell.

My next older brother and I had already decided to sit off to the side away from everyone else. We just didn't want to be among the crowd of heavy mourners. It would almost be too sad.

The service started off well. One of my hundreds of cousins gave a eulogy of my dad that hit every high point possible and had everyone in tears, including the priest and the altar boys.

Beautiful as it was, it didn't make me feel any better. This cloudy, depressing day and we're in this huge, dreary church. And I kept thinking, so what? He's gone. We're never going to see him again or talk to him again. Nothing anyone does here was going to bring him back.

I just remember the place being overwhelming dark and some of the candles going out because someone left a door open or something. After the eulogy, religion took over and the Mass crawled along at a snail's pace. Lots of needless call and response praying, random off-key singing and way too much incense. I could hardly see the altar sometimes for all the smoke.

I was so miserable I could feel pains in my stomach. I wanted to cry because everything was suddenly so meaningless. But I was ashamed and afraid it would hurt too much. Then I glanced over at my brother, and saw he was in the same condition. *That* was the lowest point of my life. Even being in jail was nothing like this. Just utter bleakness on a very bleak kind of day.

The church, Saint Mary of Perpetual Sorrow, was enormous. The altar was gigantic, cold and ornate. Above it all was a massive stained-glass window that must have been worth millions. But at the moment it looked like a huge, darkly colored headlight that had burnt out.

By the time of the consecration, I was firmly in my deep, deep end. That's when I looked up and saw the strangest thing: a thin beam of light had suddenly come through this big stained-glass window behind the altar and was illuminating the top of my father's casket.

I elbowed my brother and said: *Look…*

He saw it too. He later said the hair on the back of his neck stood up. I remember not being able to take my eyes off it. The casket glowed for a few moments and then just as suddenly, the light was gone.

We were back at an aunt's house about an hour later. The cemetery was right across the street from the church, and the graveside ceremony was just for immediate family and went quickly. My mother stayed in one of the funeral home's cars the whole time. This was no surprise as she'd always told us she could not bear to see any one of us put in the ground.

My aunt's house was so crowded by that time, it was hard to move around in any of the four downstairs rooms or the kitchen. My brother and I got stuck parking everyone else's cars and by the time we got in, it was elbow to elbow just about everywhere in the house.

The first person we looked for was our Aunt Ruby. She'd been sitting right up front with the family during the ceremony. I said to her:

"Wasn't that amazing, that beam of light coming through the stained glass and lighting up the casket?"

She looked back at me very puzzled and asked me what I was talking about. I told her the story and my brother verified everything. But my aunt hadn't seen anything and when she asked around the room, it was clear nobody else saw the light either. We were devastated.

We continued making our way through the crowd, navigating around knots of uncles and aunts holding enormous plates of cake. We were looking for our mother, but no one seemed to know where she was. That's when I really grew worried about her.

We asked a few more relatives along the way if they'd seen the beam of light, but all of them said no, politely, but also feeling a little sad for us for asking such a question.

We finally found my mother. She was sitting alone on my aunt's back porch, on a damp couch on this still damp and bleak day.

She was holding a framed photo of my father taken when he was in the Army. It had been on display at the wake and on the altar for the funeral.

I expected her to be broken in two by this time, but to my greatest surprise of the day, she was smiling. Crying, but still smiling and for some reason…almost happy.

And she was nodding and as if in prayer, saying over and over: "Now I know. Now, I understand…"

She finally looked up at us, as if she knew we'd been standing there all the time.

She smiled even wider, tears still running down her cheeks, but incredibly the light was back in her eyes.

Then she brought us both in for a hug and said: "I saw it too, boys…"

Chapter Twelve

Movie Rights Available

Reporters: When did you hear from Al again?

Steve Bruce: It was about two months after his dad died. He'd gone back to the BJ by that time.

Reporters: Did he ever tell you why he went *back* to jail?"

Steve Bruce: I'm sure my first thought was probably your first thought too: who the fuck goes back to jail if they don't have to? Only Al Ferrari, right? But I got another long letter from him after he'd returned to the joint and he explained to me why he did it—and damn, if he didn't convince me it was the right thing to do.

First, he found out that the Massachusetts Judicial System didn't really have permanent prison furloughs. Basically, they could extend them from one day up to a month, but not beyond. So even though Al was back on the streets, he had to report in monthly with the Parole Board and get his one-month furlough renewed again. He would be subject to random home checks and drug tests as well, and all for God knows how long. He told me it was really killing him that all the stuff that got him in this fix in the first place was coming back to haunt him again. It was no better than being work release or something. But, if he did the time, which was only two more months, all of that would go away. Plus, maybe it would get the DAS off his ass.

He had a second reason to go back, though. He told me he wanted to take advantage of the BJ's huge library and some of the top-notch college level courses taught there. He said he intended to take on double and even triple class loads if they let him. He wanted to absorb as much as he could, while he could. From his point of view, he was unemployed in or out of the joint. Why not get three squares a day *and* a year of college in just eight weeks?

At the end of his letter, he told me to expect a package in a month and he asked that I hold onto it for him until he could collect it himself. When it arrived, I couldn't help but look inside—after all, it was addressed to me. But the contents proved to be pure Al Ferrari.

When Al mentioned he was going to take courses at the BJ, I would have bet he meant Advanced Automotive Business Practices, where you learn not just how to be a mechanic but also how to own and run your own auto shop. That would have seemed to be a perfect career path for Al, and I knew they taught that very course there.

So, I suppose I was expecting a large manual of some sort, or a few three ring binders full of things you had to know to run an auto repair business.

Instead, the package was an ordinary 8 x 10 brown envelope.

Inside was a movie script titled: "First Blood—Dawn of the Pigmen."

Chapter Thirteen

Gun shopping with My Guardian Angel

Reporters: What was it like to finally get out of the BJ, your time fully served?

Al: It felt great. Like I just gotten out of the army or something. But I still had to keep my nose clean and more importantly, for my own sanity, get a job.

Reporters: What was it like trying to find work this time?

Al: This time, it was almost *too* easy. But that led to some issues down the road. To understand them fully, you have to know a guy named Crazy Louie Donovan.

Reporters: He's Jimmy Fitz's cousin, correct?

Al: Yes—and I'd known him since elementary school. He was an OK kid, but always pale, always with a runny nose, always absent with some kind of something. A few years later, he worked with us off and on at Palumbo's Printing. Jimmy got him a job as a puncher which was one step up from a mutter. Louie always worked hard, but just like school, he was so frail, there were a lot of missed days.

That's why it was a bit of a surprise that the day Jimmy called to congratulate me for finally getting out of the joint, he also had a job offer for me—working with Crazy Louie.

His exact words were: "Don't hang up. It pays fifty grand for a month's work…"

Reporters: Did you think it was on the level?

Al: At the time I didn't know what to think. Look, it's important to know that Louie is a great guy. But he's really out there. He's always armed with something. He's a self-taught expert on astrology, he knows the movements of all the planets and stars every night. And he's very, very into guardian angels, and not just believing in them. In fact, he was convinced he was *my* guardian angel.

Reporters: Can you expand on that?

Al: I hadn't seen Louie in a few years before he got hired at Palumbo's. Nothing had really changed. Like I said, he was still a pasty, nasally, weird looking kid—and he was still living up to his nickname. That first day, his first lunch break there, he came up to me and said: "I feel I was put on this Earth to protect you and I'll always try my best to do so."

Spooky, right? But the really crazy thing was he'd said it with such sincerity, it floored me. You could tell he meant every word of it. Way out yes, but I will admit after that, whenever he was around, I felt almost invulnerable, because I just knew no one would fuck with me or Louie would go nuts on them.

Jimmy explained that Louie now had a lucrative gig. For the past few years, in the spring, he and a buddy had been delivering a big sailboat out from Nantucket down to the Virgin Islands, basically doing all the hard work so the wealthy owner didn't have to. When autumn rolled around, they'd fly down and sail the boat back. His partner was another

Everett guy everyone called Gomez because he looked just like Johnny Astin of the Addams Family. Their price: $100,000 per trip, plus expenses. According to Jimmy, that was loose change for the guy who owned the boat.

It was easy money, but Gomez had decided to retire after the last trip, so the position was open.

And why wasn't Jimmy himself taking the job? Because he had another piece of news for me. He was engaged. His bride-to-be was from a wealthy family, but even better, she had a great job. She was the new weekend reporter on Channel 4 in Boston. Jimmy was driving a cab at the time and that's how they met. He picked her up at the airport her first day here and they got engaged a month later. All this happened while I was still in jail, but he wanted me to be out before he told me.

Now if anyone else had slung me that tale, I would say they were full of crap. But it was such a Jimmy Fitz-story, I knew it had to be true. Plus, Jimmy said she was a real dish, and I knew she would have to be because in those days Channel 4 was the ultimate babelicious channel. Her family was giving them the money to build a giant house down in Scituate and Jimmy was the general manager for the job.

I was astonished at all this, but very happy for him. I told him all those years he'd spent making an asshole of himself in front of girls must have paid off somehow.

We made plans to get together, but only after he had me promise I'd meet Louie to get more details on the Virgin Islands gig.

There's a breakfast place on the corner of Beacon St. and Noel in the middle of Lawrence, Mass named Buzzy's. A real greasy spoon, but somehow, it seemed an appropriate place to meet my guardian angel.

I hadn't seen Louie since the days at Palumbo, easily four years before, so I didn't recognize him at first. He'd morphed into Christopher Walken's younger, sicklier brother. He was so pale and drawn, he looked like he was playing Dracula in a school play. Yet he was also very wiry now and taut, like one perpetually coiled muscle.

He was wearing a brown leather jacket, bulky denim trousers, a Scally cap and mirrored sunglasses. He'd gotten a one-inch scar on his right cheek somehow, and there was a Camel dangling from his lower lip. He looked like he'd just fallen off a potato boat from Ireland.

He was jovial, though. He gave me a huge bro-hug and said: "I'm glad to see peace in my brother."

We got breakfast and he told me how wonderful the Virgin Islands were, his joke being that when school break hits, there aren't many virgins to be found down there. But then he got very serious. He poured cream into his coffee and asked me: "Do you know how to dump a body at sea and not get caught?"

This wasn't just pure Crazy Louie—this was pure Crazy Louie as an adult. And I'm sorry, but that was a scary thought.

I told him I had no idea, so he proceeded to tell me. Get six feet of chain link fence. Wrap the body in it and tie it together tight with lots of thin twine. Go out to sea about a mile or two, find a place with lots of lobster traps and, heave ho!

Crazy Louie. We were supposed to be talking about a job sailing to the Virgin Islands. Just how would dumping bodies come into this?

But the only thing I could think to ask him was why? Why was this the fool-proof method? He said because in this case, time was your friend. You dump the chain-linked body in the middle of a bunch of lobster traps. Where there are lobsters there are crabs. The crabs crawl through the openings in the chain link and devour the body. Then, within a few days, the twine will break down and the rolled-up fencing will flop open, evenly distributing the bones on the sea floor. The idea is, in just a matter of days, there will be no body, and that means nothing will ever float to the surface.

So, I asked him, what if the deceased was not an average-sized adult? What if they weighed three hundred pounds?

He told me: Then, just like in "Jaws," you're going to need a bigger boat—and a lot more chain link.

He finally started talking about the job itself. It was just as Jimmy described it: sail a very rich guy's boat from Nantucket to St Croix. If the boat gets there in one piece, they split $100,000 and sign up for the autumn cruise back at the same price. As easy as that.

It would have been the biggest payday I could have ever imagined—the thought of it staggered me a little. But I told him I had to think about it. Sue had been left alone for a very long time while I was in the joint. Only through the kindness of her boss was she able to keep her teaching assistant job despite having a husband in the penal system. I explained this to Louie and he seemed to sincerely understand, but he asked me to keep an open mind. The boat was leaving Nantucket in a month. So, I had to let him know as soon as possible.

He checked the time and then asked if I wanted to walk with him as he had to pick up some supplies for the upcoming trip. I said sure, so we walked down Beacon Street and after two blocks, took an abrupt left turn—into a gun shop.

"We need protection from the animals this time," he said as we were walking in. And for some reason, I got this idea that he was going to buy a speargun, something to shoot sharks with.

The place was wall to wall guns, a risky business in the middle of Lawrence, which was a city known for its high crime rate. The owner was a little Spanish guy. Behind him was a bird cage containing a large red parrot. They both gave us the once over as we walked in. I think I look like your ordinary left- handed Italian, very average. On the other hand, Louie looks like a vampire and dresses like a dock worker. I saw the owner inching toward his cash register where I'm sure his own personal firearm was within reach.

What was strange was, on the wall next to the parrot were two spear guns for sale. But Louie never saw them. He walked right over to one of the thick-glass counters and began gazing at a bright silver, stainless steel shotgun.

Louie called the guy over.

"Can I see that Remington Steel?"

The guy was cautious, but not hysterically. He was running a gun shop in the middle of Lawrence. He'd been through this before.

He pulled out the shotgun and handed it to Louie who took it like it was King Arthur's sword or something.

The guy told him: "For you, eleven hundred…"

Louie's eyes lit up. I know among his many peculiarities he was a very spiritual guy and had espoused peace and love for all mankind on a number of occasions. But I'd never seen him like this: a very scary looking dude who, at that moment, resembled a kid at Christmas.

In the meantime, I'd spotted a toy of my own. Hanging near the two spearguns was a 45-caliber Thompson submachine gun. Like something Al Capone or The Untouchables would have carried. A tag hanging from the barrel identified it as a true media reproduction, meaning it was built especially for a movie or a TV show—but it was a real gun. The owner scurried over, took it down and handed it to me.

So, at that moment, I've got the Thompson and Louie's got the huge stainless-steel shotgun.

And that's when Louie asked the wrong question…

He balanced the shotgun in his hands, as if about to fire it from the hip. Then he looked at the owner, deadpan, and half-whispered. "What time does that bank across the street open?"

The guy went nuts. He started screaming: "No! No! No!"

Louie realized right away he'd said the wrong thing, so he tried to explain to the guy: "No—we just want to go make a withdrawal so we can buy these guns."

But that just made it worse.

"No withdrawals!" the guy yelled back. "No guns! You must leave…"

"¡Perdedoras!" the parrot squawked, making his feelings known in Spanish. "Vamanos!"

Louie was crushed. He'd fallen hard for the stainless-steel Remington. He started to say something, but by now the guy really had had enough. Out came his own, personal sidearm, a huge .500 S&W Magnum revolver, one of the largest handguns in the world.

Louie and I quickly put down the two weapons and backed away. We were both apologizing profusely but that did not satisfy the owner. He literally chased us out of the store, both he and the parrot cursing us as we left at high speed.

Once out on the street though, Louie's ice-cold, pale demeanor returned.

"What a dick," he said. "Like I'm the first one to ever crack that joke."

I just nodded. But one question remained.

"What did you need that shotgun for anyway?" I asked him. "I mean really…"

"To shoot pirates," Louie replied very casually. "They're everywhere down there. They're like fucking animals."

Chapter Fourteen

Stealing the Titanic

Reporters: When did you hear from Al again?

Steve Bruce: It was about a month after I'd received his last package. He didn't call me, my old partner, Joey Kelly did. He'd been working a private detail at a museum in the seaport area, the place where they were showing a huge piece of the Titanic at the time. It's near the Mystic River. Harrington Square? Do you know where that is?

Reporters: The intersection of four main streets, it's half in Boston, half in Everett, right?

Steve Bruce: Yep—city lines cut it right down the middle. And that's where they put the new seaport museum, but it's also where the municipal court is located, a place I'm so familiar with. Then right across the street is Kelsey's, a bar where all the Everett guys hung out. And next to that, the St. Don Bosco Home for Little Wanderers. It's an orphanage for boys, and a real dump.

So, Joey is working a traffic detail outside Kelsey's when a security guard from the museum comes running across the square yelling that someone just stole a piece of the Titanic. That someone had actually reached behind the protective glass and broke off a piece of the famous ship's hull.

Joey called it in to the precinct, then ran back to the museum with the guard, but the perp was long gone by then. Still, all the building's alarms had been struck and all the doors had been shut and locked, keeping everyone who was inside the building at the time, stuck there. And that's when the real crap-storm started.

For some bizarre reason, Joey's call back to the precinct had prompted someone to label the incident a Class A Felony, theft of a priceless artifact. And because, at least in theory, the Boston police should have been the ones protecting it, and seeing that half the stolen property technically belonged to Great Britain, this in turn caused someone else to trigger the alarm for Boston's super-SWAT unit, the Urgent Response Team. Although usually called only if a bomb had gone off or if there was a threat of terrorism to the city, five armored vehicles descended on the square nevertheless, carrying a lot of Boston cops dressed in camo gear and helmets.

But it wasn't over yet, because all this activity lit up the Greater Boston Area Mutual Aid Law Enforcement Broadcast System which led the Everett PD to send all their anti-crime guys to the scene, three patrol cars full, also wearing camo gear. And then, finally and for reasons no one ever explained, alarms in the five fire stations nearest to the square went off simultaneously. Each station sent three trucks to the scene; they arrived about the same time as reporters from every major TV News channel in Boston.

Although I'm sure it looked impressive, if you like that sort of thing, it was all for nothing, really. The museum was searched but the perp was not found; obviously he'd made it out of the building before the doors had been locked. Traffic was fucked up for hours in both Boston and Everett, plus they'd managed to scare the doody out of a hundred little school kids on a field trip to the museum who wound up sealed inside for almost two hours before things got sorted out. This in turn caused a small army of angry parents to arrive in the overcrowded square, demanding that because their children were so traumatized by what was happening inside, their school had to arrange counseling services for all of them, free of charge.

Now, in one of the many odd things that happened that day, Jimmy Fitz's weekend reporter wife happened to be filling in for her weekday counterpart's afternoon shift. It turned out she was part of the media horde that arrived at the museum about the same time as the fire trucks.

As a foreshadowing of her future endeavors, not only had Jimmy's cute wife—her professional name was Monica Chase—somehow managed to get herself inside the museum, which at that moment was surrounded by cops and armored SWAT trucks, she also talked her way into its video room. With only the museum's security chief and a Boston Police captain looking on, she was one of the first people to see the closed-circuit security footage of the Titanic incident.

It wasn't exactly the Zapruder film, but for some people, it showed enough. Inside a dimly lit, almost solemn room, a line of museum customers could be seen slowly filing past the Titanic display, which was actually a billboard-sized portion of the famously doomed ship's hull. It had been placed inside a gigantic glass tank with vent holes on the sides and a continuous shower of saltwater deluging it from above to avoid further deterioration.

About a minute into the tape, several adults pass by the display, and they appear to have been drinking. Then comes two strollers with two moms and two kids. Suddenly one of the kids erupts in an ear-piercing tantrum. It was so loud, it set off the second kid as well. It's obvious that the unexpected shrieks distract the attention of just about everyone in the display hall, including the security guard. That's when one of the drunk adults comes back into the frame, reaches through one of the tank's vent holes and clearly breaks off a piece of the ship's hull. Then he moves on as the kids' dueling outbursts continue to take center stage.

The Boston Police captain asked the museum security chief if the thief looked familiar. He was mid-to-late 20s, average build, dark complexion, most likely left-handed. The security boss stated that he'd never seen the man before.

But Monica Chase had.

She immediately left the museum and called Jimmy Fitz down at their new house in Scituate. She told him what she'd seen—and he in turn immediately called me. I'd just put the news on when the phone rang and I had been able to read the headlines at least. Once Jimmy knew I was up to speed on the strange situation at the museum, he asked me this question: "Guess which left-handed resident of Everett just stole a piece of history?"

Monica had told Jimmy there was no mistaking it—it was Al, caught on video, pulling off a chunk of the Titanic's hull. Even worse, Jimmy told me the Boston cops had decided this was their case and were presently running the security footage up to their HQ with the intention of putting it on TV and asking civilians to be on the look-out for the perp. Then Jimmy said what I already knew: as soon as someone made the link, our old friend Al was going to be arrested and imprisoned once again. And as this really *was* a Class A felony, there was a good chance he wasn't going back to that community college at Bedford Junction.

Reporters: So, you gave him a heads up? Or a head start?

Steve Bruce: Neither. I called him to tell him that they had him on security tape doing what he did and that he should turn himself in and if he did, I'd go in with him. I talked to him for all of two minutes, when he finally said, okay. He'd be ready when I got there.

The problem was, there was almost nothing I could actually do for him once he surrendered. Incredibly he *still* had that Department of Adult Services thing hanging around his neck. He'd done his time on his auto theft violation, but it turned out his lawyer fucked him, collecting his fee *then* telling Al that he actually had to follow the DAS guidelines until…well, forever. That's the way Judge Troy had written the court order.

Now, if he went back to jail for the Titanic thing, he would not be employed and those pricks at DAS were likely to run him up on that alone. If that hadn't been the situation, I thought maybe I could get a judge to give him bail or maybe even get him released on personal cognizance, at least for a while.

But, either way, Al was going back to prison.

I drove to his place in Everett as fast as I could, but by the time I got there, Al was gone. And so was Sue, but it was apparent she'd left a long time before.

The apartment was cleared out, no phone, no lights. The refrigerator unplugged. I'd gotten to know Sue a little bit during all this, and she definitely had the woman's touch. It was obvious she hadn't been in this place in months.

I was about to call Al's cousin Johnny, the Registry cop, when one of the neighbors walked in. Little Italian guy, blackened stogie hanging from his mouth. He had a big manila envelope under his arm.

"Are you Al's friend, the cop?" he asked me.

"I'm a cop," I told him.

He handed me the envelope and said: "Al wanted me to give you this and to say that's he's sorry he had to leave before you got here."

I asked him where Al went, hoping the answer would be to turn himself in on his own. But I knew there was little chance of that.

"He just caught on with an outfit that sails rich people's yachts down the Caribbean for the season," the guy said. "He'll be gone six weeks and he said he'd get in touch with you when he gets back, if he doesn't send you a postcard first."

The big envelope had my name on it. I had one sad thought as the guy handed it to me. If only it was some kind of confession—something typically Al and written in long hand on yellow legal pad paper. Or a clear admission of guilt and a promise to clearly own up to it. *That* would help him a lot now, especially before he got caught as a fugitive.

But the contents of the envelope were anything but a confession.

Instead, inside was another movie script written by Al.

This one was called "Blood on the Sun—High Noon of the Pig-men."

Chapter Fifteen

How to Un-Sink a Ship

Interview with Johnny "Jackie D" Daniels, friend and co-worker of Al Ferrari, ECM Talent Offices, Beverly Hills, Ca.

Reporters: There are many different versions of what we've come to call The Titanic Incident. We know for sure that a piece of the Titanic was stolen—and it was probably stolen by Al Ferrari. So, our question is, do you agree it was a strange time for him to commit yet another crime?

Daniels: Well, I can't answer that because I disagree with your overall premise. It wasn't a crime Al committed that day. It was an act of mercy and humanity.

Reporters: We've seen the security footage. His actions appear pretty brazen and...

Daniels, (interrupting): But how much of the museum's security footage did you actually see? Just the angle of him breaking off a tiny piece of that old, failed boat? Or did you see the exterior footage that shows Al with the orphans?

Reporters, (after a brief discussion): We saw only the footage from interior cameras. We saw no orphans.

Daniels: Well, that's just another way of saying you didn't see all the footage.

Reporters, (another brief discussion): We can't disagree. So, please tell us how orphans play into this.

Daniels: You first have to know about the neighborhood where the museum is located. It's a big and new and beautiful building, but it's right across the street from Kelsey's Bar, a place where my *grandfather* used to drink—*as a kid.* It's definitely not big and new and beautiful anymore. And right next to *that,* is the Saint Bosco Home for Wayward Waifs or something. It's right out of Dickens.

So, Al and I had been working at this telemarketing company in Saugus, selling aluminum siding over the phone to the elderly. It was such a scam I remember Al saying he had to be very careful reporting it as a real job to those assholes at DAS. Everyone there was paid to basically bilk money out of little old ladies. Twenty of us in the owner's basement, working the phones. It really *was* a sweat shop, but the pay wasn't bad.

Anyway, the owner was this Filipino dude from Charlestown named Juan-Juan. And he was nuts about anything British because his wife was half-British. He was known for throwing money around so when the Titanic thing came to town, he gave us the afternoon off and bought all of us tickets to go see the thing.

None of us gave a crap about the fucking Titanic—you can take my word on that. To us it was an afternoon off with pay. It was only later did we find out the tickets cost $50—each. Lot of money then, lot of money now. That's what they were charging to get in to see what I thought was this big piece of fucking rust.

116

Anyway, we had lunch at Kelsey's and we all got pretty hammered. Kelsey seemed to have more Irish flags hanging up than usual, his way of rubbing it in to the Brits across the street. I can still hear him saying: "It sunk. What's all the bullshit about?"

But when it was time to go, Kelsey being the prick that he is, told us he'd sell us cans of beer to bring with us—but the price was two bucks a can! Everyone bought at least one can though.

Reporters: But why would you take beer into a museum?

Daniels: It wasn't for the museum. We're not animals. It was for waiting in the line *outside* the museum. That's another part of this story that few people know—and that's why I'm glad I can give Al's side of what really happened that day.

The line went around the block all the way up the street to the steps of the courthouse. There had to be at least three hundred people in front of us and that was just those waiting outside. Who knows how many more were lined up inside?

So, we knew it was going to be a long wait and we took the beer just to keep the buzz going, you know? And it was okay for a while—but then it started to snow.

Now the next part I wouldn't have believed unless I saw it myself—but I did. As soon as the first snowflakes hit the pavement, the door to the orphanage flew open and all these kids in ragamuffin clothes came flooding out, carrying tin cans. They come running across the street to the line of people waiting to get in the museum and start begging for money.

At first I thought it was a scam because of the way they coordinated this and how certain kids took certain parts of the line—it was obvious they'd done this sort of thing before. But it was actually pretty sad, because we could hear them saying the money was not for them, not all of them anyway. They told us they just wanted to raise fifty bucks so one lucky kid among them could get in to see a piece of history.

But all the people at the front of the line were cheap pricks and by the time the kids get to us, we can only give them about five bucks, nowhere near what it costs to get into the place.

We left them in tears.

Reporters: When you finally got into the exhibit, what was it like?

Daniels: As it turned out, it was pretty cool. It started with a kind of history lesson about what happened. I swear to God, before this I thought the Titanic had been torpedoed, but I'm a product of the Everett School System. Anyway, when you read the facts it's kind of humbling because it really hits you how many people died on that thing just because of a fucking iceberg. Then you walk into the display hall itself and it's all darkened and solemn like a church. And that's where they have a big piece of the actual ship. It's like twenty feet by ten feet, and they show you on a diagram where it was located on the hull. They had it on an angle inside this giant glass box with water running all over it, to keep it hydrated, I guess.

All this was surrounded by a fancy velvet rope. And watching over everybody and everything was a gigantic security guard who could have been Mike Tyson's brother.

The first few seconds inside that hall was almost a religious experience for me—but that ended when these two women followed us in, each with a kid in a stroller. And they start screaming their lungs out.

The longer it went on, the worse it got. These kids were savages, screaming fucking savages. First one, then they both flip out. It got so bad the security guard left his post and tried to calm them down. But then both mothers turned on him. They were nutty broads from Southie and he's a Black guy, and that's usually a bad combination. Anyway, they start cursing him like crazy, he calls for back-up, and now all of a sudden there's a huge commotion inside this darkened, almost spiritual chamber.

That's when Al pulled me aside and said: these rich assholes are in here not paying an ounce of attention, while those poor kids are out there, no parents, no family, begging for scraps.

No sooner had he said that when Al very calmly reached around the pane of glass protecting the hull and tore off a piece maybe seven inches long and shoved it in his pocket. I asked him what the fuck he was doing, and he explained that he planned to give it to those poor kids outside because it was an actual piece of history and that would mean a lot more to them than just seeing it for a minute or two.

It was totally screwy logic, but I couldn't argue with him. Plus, we were still pretty buzzed. A second after he filched it, we were quietly exiting the building. But once back on the outside, I looked at Al and son-of-a-bitch, he has this big red stain running down the front of his pants. It looked like he'd been shot and was bleeding, not a too unusual sight in this part of town. But he was actually bleeding rust, from the piece of wreck he had in his pocket. It just looked exactly like blood.

There was a vendor nearby selling sausages in the snow. Al asked him for a few napkins, but he said he'd had to buy something first. So, Al calmly ordered a sausage in a grilled roll and extra peppers and then handed it to me: it was excellent by the way. Meanwhile, Al had grabbed a hand full of napkins and convinced the guy to sell him an old plastic bag the peppers used to come in. He put the piece of the ship in the bag with some snow. It was funny because at first it looked like he was carrying a goldfish. Only on closer examination could you tell what it really was.

Al used the napkins to clean the rust off his pants as best he could, then he and I and a couple of the other guys walked over with him to the poor kids home.

The orphans were in tears again, but this time with gratitude when Al gave them the piece of the big ship. They were all crowded around the front door, snow coming down, crying for joy. They didn't know us or our names but that was okay because Al was like an angel to them at that moment and from the way they looked, they needed some kind of miracle in their sad little lives.

I remember going home that night feeling I'd actually seen someone do something really good for someone else and that I was going to sleep like a baby. But then I dreamed about hearing a lot of sirens and next thing I know Officer Bruce is calling on the phone.

He asked if I'd seen or heard from Al. I told him no. He told me that Al was in very big trouble now—and if he took off, there might not be any way of his coming back from it.

The next day, word was all over Everett that Al had skipped town with Jimmy Fitz's cousin, Crazy Louie.

And the last anyone saw Crazy Louie, he was buying a silver double-barrel shotgun, a Thompson machine gun and a cage of some kind at a gun shop in the middle of Lawrence.

***

Reporters: When did you hear the conclusion of the Titanic story? The real ending, that is?

Steve Bruce: About two weeks after Al disappeared. I was at the courthouse testifying in a drug case and during the break I jumped over to

Kelsey's for lunch. He told me the whole story and, I must admit, it was a bit disappointing.

Those little assholes from the Bosco orphanage were basically running a scam. There'd be a group of them out there every day, begging for money to get inside the museum when they were actually spending it on cigarettes and beer.

Those same urchins duped Al into feeling bad for them, so he steals a piece of the freaking Titanic for them, and they make money off it, while he goes on the lam.

Reporters: How do you know they made money or if that's even a true story?

Steve Bruce: Because I saw it myself. The piece of the Titanic everyone was shitting kittens about is sitting in Kelsey's, in the aquarium above the bar, the one with the sunken British flag and the family of piranhas. They *sold* it to him. Check it out for yourselves…"

PART 3

Chapter Sixteen

Voyage of The Last Chance

Reporters: How did you find out what eventually happened to Al down in the Caribbean?

Steve Bruce: For me it started, as always, with the phone ringing in the middle of the night. About a week after he disappeared, the Boston cops finally put out an international APB on Al. About a week after that, a friend of a friend of a friend asked a cop down in St. Croix in the U.S. Virgin Islands to give me a call about a persons-missing-at-sea report that had crossed his desk.

He told me the previous night the remains of two boats had washed up near a place called Bay Cove on the northern side of the island. Two cops were sent to investigate. They first found what was left of a sizable sailboat that had caught fire at sea. The broken main mast, the crumpled steering bridge and the starboard galley was all that remained of the burnt vessel.

The guy explained that finding the remnants of yachts along St. Croix's coastline was not unusual. This part of the Caribbean was a hot spot for the mega-rich and their expensive boats, so it was no surprise that a few of them would run into trouble near the island over the years. High seas, bad weather, or even just running out of gas, many of their occupants were saved by the Coast Guard or passing boaters. But it didn't end well for everybody.

That's because there was another scourge out there: Pirates. The cop told me they operate out of dozens of smaller islands in the area, places that hardly show up on a map. They stalk big yachts like wolves;

only when the victim was out in the middle of nowhere do they strike. It was easy after that. Plunder the boat, kill any witnesses, and make a clean getaway. The empty yacht wanders aimlessly for days or even weeks, the elements battering it, sometimes catching it on fire. Finally, the pieces wash up on beaches like Bay Cove. Again, not unusual.

It was what the St. Croix cops found another hundred yards down the beach that was *highly* unusual. It was a large Boston Whaler speedboat, a favorite of the local pirates, dashed against the rocks of the cove's jetty. There were seven dead bodies on board. All of them still in their seats, still wearing their safety harnesses; all of them shot multiple times and burnt to a crisp.

The St. Croix cop faxed me the incident report. The condition of the bodies on the Whaler and the boat itself indicated it had been involved in a violent clash at sea probably 48 hours before. The report stated the sailboat may have also been involved.

But most puzzling, while the bodies on the Whaler had been charred beyond recognition, they'd also been shot with at least three different kinds of ammunition, including enormous shotgun rounds and 45-caliber machine gun bullets.

Later that day, a U.S. Coast Guard vessel found four people who claimed to have witnessed the bizarre battle at sea. They were on a deep-sea night-fishing charter when they got caught in the storm, which was later described as a strong, but localized squall. According to their testimony, the pirates in the Whaler appeared out of nowhere, but so did the huge sailboat, which they said was painted yellow and had two armed men on board. The witnesses emphasized these men saved their lives by ramming the pirates' boat before it got to their fishing charter. A gun battle then broke out and both boats caught on fire. But while the Boston Whaler disappeared into the squall, the witnesses said, the Good Samaritans' sailboat went down right in front of them. The crew of the fishing charter were unable to reach either man, but they were able to get the boat's name: "The Last Chance."

That was the name of the boat Al and Crazy Louie had been sailing to the Islands.

I asked the St. Croix cop what he thought of the story. He told me that while anything was possible, it was not unknown for drug smugglers to transfer their products at night in bad weather, thus reducing their chances of getting caught. And sometimes more than two vessels are involved. He added that drug deals can go bad in any kind of weather.

He promised to stay in touch, but after waiting another two days, I called him back. He was courteous but obviously busy with other things. He told me a judge had read the incident report and concluded everyone involved in the gun battle—the people on the Whaler and the yellow sailboat—had to be deceased. Officially, the file would stay open. But for all intents and purposes, the case was closed.

I felt I had to be the one to explain all this to Al's family. They'd been in touch almost hourly with the Everett Police public affairs person, looking for any little bit of news on Al and Louie. I knew this new development would be all over Everett in a few hours. But I didn't feel right having the department PA deliver the bad news to Al's family, especially his mother.

So, I drove down to Barman's Court and parked out front of 4A. I saw Al's mother peeking at me through the blinds. Our eyes met and, in that moment, she knew why I was there. She let me in, and I told her the whole story. There were tears for sure—more at the inevitability of it all. I told her that Al was a good person who just had the bad luck to run afoul of the law in the oddest ways. He did actual time for a stupid reason, and that would sour anybody. This time he tried to stay one step ahead of the law and ultimately that led to his demise.

But as his brother said later that evening, at least Al didn't live a boring life.

When I told Al's mother I'd help in any way I could, she handed me Sue's new phone number. An hour later, I was going through the same tearful scene, just this time in Sue's apartment condo in Malden. I took the next day off from work and helped her retrieve all of Al's belongings from his mother's house.

That's when Al's mother told me the family had decided they wanted a *scrigno vuoto*—an "empty casket" funeral for Al. Basically, another name for a memorial service, his mother insisted on a casket of the same size and quality as the one they'd buried her husband in. It had to be exact right down to the last detail. When I asked her why, she told me the story of seeing the ray of sun break through the somberness at her husband's funeral and lighting his casket—and she hoped the same would happen for Al.

How could I argue with that?

Johnny O'Neil, the ex-funeral director, had landed back on his feet and was by this time making another fortune selling real estate. He provided another masterwork casket to Al's family. It traveled to the church and was carried up the church steps by almost the same group of pallbearers as before. And as luck would have it, the day was gloomy and overcast, just like the day they said goodbye to Al's father.

The church was packed this time, too. Everyone in attendance had by now heard the story of the miraculous beam of light coming through the church's massive stained-glass window that day, anointing Al's father's casket, but seen only by Al, his brother, and his mother.

I can tell you the priest had an attentive audience that day, everyone waiting for the same thing to happen again. They sat through the service, hearing the same prayers, singing the same songs—but there was no miraculous light. The church remained dark and joyless for the entire ceremony. And as soon as the attendees all got outside, the sky opened up and the rain came down in buckets, soaking everyone as they ran for their cars.

Jimmy Fitz had flown back to Boston for the service along with his TV reporter wife. They'd recently moved to Los Angeles after she got a job on KLAA, the news station all the stars watched. I didn't see Jimmy but from what I heard, he was a mess. He was drinking non-stop during the entire visit and locked himself in the hotel's bathroom twice, scaring the crap out of his wife.

But no one could blame him. He was just another domino that got toppled in this whole sad affair. A simple and kind gesture of getting Al another job had turned into him getting his dear friend and his cousin killed. He told everyone he knew he would never be the same, that his life had become very hard living after it all went down. Heavily medicated, he'd managed to stay through the smaller, more private service held for his cousin, Louie. But he only made it to the sermon at Al's funeral before he had to be taken out of the church; the emotions were just too much. The almost always exuberant Irishman was now a dark and troubled drunk.

The day after, Al's cousin, Johnny the Registry cop, went to an Everett City Council meeting; his father-in-law was the chairman. After about fifteen minutes of discussion, a motion was brought forth that Glendale Park, a ballpark close to where Al grew up, be renamed "Al Ferrari Field" in his memory—not the first time a notorious citizen of Everett had been so honored. The measure passed unanimously.

About two weeks later they held a fund raiser for Al's mother at Kelsey's. The place was overflowing to the point where the fire department had to shut it down.

But between sincere donations and those resulting from Kelsey's relentless arm twisting—both virtually and physically—they raised more than $50,000, enough for Al's mother to pay off the mortgage for the house on Barman's Court.

Chapter Seventeen

Wat de kikvorsman zag
(What the Frogmen Saw)

Translated from the daily watch log of the HNLMS *Makkon*, Royal Netherlands Navy, recorded 0520 hours, May 25, 1989. Subject: Suspected drowning victim observed by MARSOF underwater team, M-Squadron.

Our frigate was patrolling the coast of Her Majesty's Territory Saba Island supporting two M-Squadron combat divers working on a mine detection drill.

The two divers were approximately 25 meters off the north coast of Saba when they spotted a human figure about five meters below them, near the sandy bottom.

The divers believed they'd come upon the drowned body of a Caucasian male in his twenties. It appeared partially entangled in two long strands of sargassum seaweed, one around the head and neck, the other around the waist. (Captain's note: M-Squadron's training manual states that a body entangled in seaweed has most likely been immersed for an extended period of time.)

The divers drew closer and both stated for a moment they thought they'd come upon a murder victim. The way the long piece of seaweed was wrapped around the head and neck, "almost like a scarf." Plus, they were looking down at a clear bottom. Sargassum seaweed grows on the surface of the ocean, not the bottom.

The speculation of a homicide ended a few moments later, when the "dead man" did a complete roll over and realized the two divers were just above him.

He waved to them, but with his fists, because both his hands were full of coins. The divers reported some of the coins were spilling out of the spaces between his fingers and falling back into the sand below, that's how many the man was holding. At that point, the subject secured the long pieces of seaweed around his waist and his head and quickly swam away.

The divers surfaced and watched the man reach the shore. They stated he was quickly surrounded by, judging how they were dressed, a small, mixed group of locals and tourists and "still wearing his seaweed wraps, was mildly greeted like some kind of reluctant hero."

At that point, the M-Squadron combat divers radioed back to our ship to brief us on the encounter and then resumed their exercise.

Chapter Eighteen

The Secret of Pigeon Cove

Reporters: Did you ever get to see the Dutch Navy report?

Steve Bruce: Not until after the fact. Had I seen it when it first happened, things might have turned out differently, but here we are.

Reporters: You said earlier that everything changed for you on June 1, 1989. What happened to you that day?

Steve Bruce: That was the day the City of Everett was going to officially rename Glendale Park to Al Ferrari Field. They had a big crowd on hand because there were a lot of Ferraris living in Everett at the time, and most of them were very well known. The mayor was going to make a speech, two youth football teams were going to play the field's inaugural game and the Everett High School band was going to do a few numbers. Fireworks were scheduled for later that night.

The media had been alerted and two local Boston TV trucks showed up, along with a few newspaper reporters. I arrived a little late because I had a hard time finding a parking spot with all the hubbub going on. Luckily, I got a seat in the last row of folding chairs they'd set up for Al's friends and family.

The mayor and the whole city council had arrived by that time. They were testing the microphones on the podium, the Registry's color guard was standing by, waiting for their cue. It was just as someone started playing the National Anthem over the loudspeaker system that my beeper went off.

It was Jimmy Fitz, out in LA. He must have known what was happening in Everett that day, but I didn't have a clue why he'd be beeping me.

There was a pay phone nearby. I dialed his number, but he didn't even let me say hello.

Instead, he just yelled: "Stop the ceremony!"

Reporters: And you were in the Caribbean 24 hours later?

Steve Bruce: Yes, I was. Before that, the closest I'd come to that part of the world was Florida. But soon after that phone call with Jimmy Fitz, I was on a flight out of Logan Airport on my way to a place called Saba Island.

I'd never heard of it, never mind knowing where it was. Turns out it's down near the Virgin Islands, but it's run by the Dutch. More important for us, though, Saba Island is only about a hundred miles east of St. Croix.

Jimmy Fitz got a phone call from someone on Saba Island named Jumbo Zal. He claimed to know Al and said Al was alive and living on this Saba Island. He said Al and his friend got mixed up with some pirates and only Al survived, but he was in good health. Then, this Jumbo guy tells Jimmy that Al wants to turn himself in, but Al's insisting he needs to speak to me first—in person. Imagine my surprise.

I put a scenario together on the flight down and thought it was plausible: Al got caught up in a drug deal involving pirates when he and Crazy Louie reached the Caribbean, and they got an unpleasant sample of what the violent life could be like down there. Al somehow survived and wound up a hundred miles away on an island no one's ever heard of. Fearing the cops would *really* be coming for him this time, he decided to just disappear, or wait until he was declared dead or… or who knows? But his brother was right: Al sure didn't lead a boring life.

At that moment, neither was I.

The trip down to Saba was hardly a direct flight. I flew in a huge jet to Miami, then switched to a smaller commuter jet to fly to St. Croix. From there I had to get a special waiver from the local civilian air administrator before I could buy a ticket for the flight to Saba, about 40 minutes away. I was assured this was all just routine. But then I saw what I'd be flying in.

It was a very small, prop-driven puddle-jumper. Eight passenger seats, seven of them empty. Just me and the pilot. Only when we were airborne, and bouncing around in the brisk, tropical turbulence, did I find out why the need for the waiver. Almost casually the pilot yelled back to me: "Did you know Saba Island has the shortest commercial runway in the world?"

I have veloxrotaphobia, fear of roller coasters. I found this out as a kid after just a couple vomit-inducing rides. I finally got over it, though. All it took was going in for a landing on Saba Island.

It was like being at the top of the tallest roller coaster imaginable—something from a nightmare—and then plunging almost straight down towards this dot of an island in the middle of the sea that looks like it's all rocks and cliffs and jungle.

It turns out the airstrip was barely 1,000 feet long, halfway up a mountain. And the pilot had told me just before our descent that there were steep cliffs at both ends of it, so every landing had to be perfect. At that point, I just closed my eyes and prayed.

We came in on two big bounces. I unwisely opened my eyes only to see the runway in front of us shrinking very rapidly. I was sure we weren't going to make it when the pilot finally reversed his engines and stood on the brakes—and after what seemed like an eternity, we came to a stop about ten feet from the edge.

Goodbye, veloxrotaphobia.

Hello, fear of flying.

Saba is one of the smallest islands in the Caribbean; a mere postage stamp compared to St. Eustatius and St. Maarten nearby.

It was actually an extinct volcano, and basically one whole mountain, which accounted for the perilous cliffs and a 360-degree rocky coastline. The road out of the airport was impossibly steep and covered by thick jungle. My cab had to stop twice to avoid hitting stray goats and both times I was sure we were going to roll backwards and plunge off one of those cliffs.

But even after that, I couldn't lose the feeling there was something special about this place. Hundreds of neat, little white houses dotted the sides of the mountain. The higher we climbed, the more the air smelled like a tropical perfume. Whenever the jungle cleared, the views were spectacular; it was like you could see hundreds of miles in every direction. And I swear I could hear music just kind of floating around everywhere.

For a long time, Saba had no beaches, just its rough, circular, rocky shoreline with no sand. That changed years before when nearby St. Maarten donated a hundred tons of sand for a place on the northern edge of Saba called Pigeon Cove. That became Saba's one and only beach. And it was here, I would later learn, that the Dutch frogmen first saw the man underwater, wrapped in seaweed, swimming with his hands full of coins.

***

When I arrived at Pigeon Cove, I could see at least a couple hundred people, some in the water, some sunbathing, others just hanging out on the beach. A dozen brilliantly colorful cottages ringed the half-moon-shaped cove and there was a bar right up on the water's edge. It was barely 11 in the morning, but the place was packed.

Another business was located next to the bar—and it too was bustling with customers. But they didn't serve food or booze here. Their business was beach prospecting, as in using commercial metal detectors to scour the sands for lost treasure.

But why here, on the smallest island in the Caribbean with possibly the smallest beach in the world? I understood only after the cab driver told me about Fidel Castro's Missing Yacht.

As the story went, back in 1961, the Cuban dictator, who was also an avid numismatist, secretly purchased a huge collection of unusual coins from someone on St Maarten. Castro sent his private yacht to retrieve the collection, but on the night of April 1, 1961, the vessel was hit by a storm off Pigeon Cove and sank.

More than $200,000 in various coins went down with it, but a sizable number of them had made their way to shore over the years, especially around Pigeon Cove. If someone was lucky enough to have a metal detector on hand, there was a good chance they were going find something there—and maybe *a lot* of something.

Or at least that was the story.

The cabbie was quick to add that no one could recall Castro's yacht sinking off Pigeon Cove or anywhere else near the island. And was Fidel Castro really a coin collector? And, did he even *have* a yacht?

So, I asked the cabbie where the story came from.

At that moment, a figure wearing a piece of seaweed on his head emerged from the small white shack behind the bar.

The cabbie pointed to him and said, "Ask him. His name is Al…"

***

I don't want to say it was like meeting a ghost, because in all that time, I don't think I was ever really convinced that Al was dead.

But now, here he was, after a very awkward buddy hug, sitting across from me at a picnic table on the beach, a massive sun umbrella keeping out the rays. He was rail thin, had long hair and a beard and was wearing a speedo. His headgear, which looked slightly like a crown, was indeed made of seaweed.

I wanted to know so much from him. What happened that night off St. Croix? How did he make it to Saba Island? Why had he decided now was the time to return home?

But first of all, I wanted to know what was up with this "coins from Castro's yacht" bullshit?

"We make a lot of money renting metal detectors," he explained. "Normally, I go out every morning with a couple handfuls of mostly quarters and sprinkle them around the beach. Then the people and tourists arrive, rent a metal detector for $30 an hour and are excited to find a couple bucks in quarters."

The scheme was pure Al. But, he went on…

"But after a while we realized we were throwing around way more quarters than people were finding. I finally figured out that a lot of them were going out with the tide. You've got a pretty strong tidal pull inside the cove because of its half-moon shape. So, every other day I go out for an early morning swim and find the missing quarters. They're always in the same place, about twenty feet out from the low-tide mark, just waiting there, neatly stacked by a whirlpool or something."

And the seaweed crown?

I think it might have been the first time I ever saw Al laugh. Like really laugh.

"Oh, this?" he said feeling around his headgear. "Hey, there's no excuse for not looking good."

Chapter Nineteen

A Real Guardian Angel

From a Transcript of Remarks by Al Ferrari as recorded by Steve Bruce, date unknown.

It all started with the parrot.

Old Bones Jones. He was a beautiful bird to look at. His feathers were not just bright red, blue and green but also vivid yellow, orange and violet. He had a gigantic beak and his eyes—deep, deep black— were always staring at you, always following you around.

Louie had bought him from the gun shop owner in Lawrence the same day he went back to purchase the stainless-steel Remington and the working replica of the vintage Thompson. Louie told the guy that he was taking a trip to the Caribbean and needed a translator. The guy didn't get the joke but sold him the bird anyway.

It was obvious from the start that while the parrot barely tolerated me, he was devoted to Louie. When he was awake, he rarely left Louie's side—or more accurately, his shoulder. That's where he was the first time I saw him after Louie bought him. Perched on Louie's left shoulder, eating saltines smeared with peanut butter. The first thing he said on seeing me was: "Who's the loser?"

This was also the first time I saw "The Last Chance." It was an enormous yellow sailboat, 55 feet long, with gigantic sails and a soar- ing main mast. There was room to sleep a dozen, plus crew, and fully stocked bars on every level including the sailing bridge.

I thought its name was very poetic. The night of the Titanic inci- dent, when I realized the shit was going to hit the fan, I drove my car to Wood's Hole and caught the last ferry to Nantucket. It turned out to be a nauseating trip, storming the whole way with waves breaking right over the nose of this thing. People were throwing up. Kids screaming for their parents. At one point they told us not to touch anything metal in case we got hit by lightning.

But we made it, and I stayed in the dumpiest motel on Nantucket that night—and it still cost me more than three hundred bucks, which I barely had. And all this time I was convinced every LEO from the State Police on down were looking for me—or even worse, tailing me.

I finally made it through the night and showed up at the appointed dock in Old Town, Nantucket, and there's Louie, as always looking like he was in need of an immediate blood transfusion. But he was all smiles, finally a buccaneer with a fucking parrot on his shoulder. He was even wearing a ruffle-sleeved shirt.

He said he was glad I changed my mind and decided to take the gig. That's when the parrot took his cue and squawked again: "Who's the loser?"

And I remember in that one brief moment, wondering if this was really a good idea.

But then I heard the bare wisp of a siren far, far away, and that was enough for me to throw my suitcase on board and tell Louie: "Let's get out of here…"

Thirty minutes later we'd left Nantucket Harbor and had turned south.

Louie showed me some basic duties I'd be responsible for. It was nothing crazy. Make sure all the rope spools were tight, make sure the bilge pump worked when it should and make sure everything on board that had to be charged up was done regularly. Other than that, and keeping the coffee warm, I was just along for the ride.

The sailboat was really nice. It was built in Sweden by the famous Lürssen Boatworks. Louie told me it cost the owner $20 million new, and I had no problem believing that. Almost everything on board was automated and controlled by a state-of-the-art Mac computer, which I was not in love with at first, but which I grew to adore. It had one of the new-fangled GPS units attached to it and did a great job keeping us on course, checking the compass every ten minutes or so. It also watched over our electrical systems, regulated our fuel and oil consumption and had up to the minute marine weather forecasts.

Once underway, Louie and I went to the very impressive steering bridge—yes, TV and a full bar included—and sat in the captains' chairs because that was the coolest place on the boat to be. As for the actual minute-by-minute steering, that was being done by the Mac as well.

It was like a dream that first day, a good one. The farther we got away from Nantucket and New England the better I felt. And the better I felt, the more I calmed down. Louie revealed that since taking the boat gig three years ago, he'd read just about every book he could find about sailing in the Caribbean, including many of the old buccaneer stories— literally Pirates of the Caribbean. He told me a bunch of these stories, and I was surprised how really spooky they were and much more disturbing than your usual ghost stories.

It was strange, but his tales gave me something else to think about other than jail or the cops chasing me. The way Louie was able to weave these haunted narratives with the intoxicating beauty of the part of the world we were about to enter—it was fascinating. Maybe even hypnotic.

***

Night fell, and that's when Louie brought the bird up to the steering bridge. Apparently parrots like to sleep a lot and this one was no different.

But as soon as the cover came off his cage, he was wide awake, flapping his wings and cawing: "Who's this loser? He looks like a fucking loser…"

Louie fed him some more saltines and peanut butter and that stopped the squawking. He told me not to take it personally, but it was hard not to. Louie had just taught the bird to speak English. Who else could he have been talking about while the bird was learning his second language?

But then Louie showed me what the bird could *really* do.

First, he explained that pirates liked parrots for many reasons, one of them being they were like watchdogs—or better yet, a watch-geese.

"They have great eyesight," he told me. "Especially at night. They have a little bit of infra-red vision like seagulls do and a great sense of smell. But they also have great hearing and seem to sense things a few seconds before they happen. Sometimes they'll even verbalize it to you. That's the advantage of having a talking bird. Pirate captains had them on board because they could warn of enemy ships approaching or even obstacles in the water. I'm telling you they're as smart as some humans…"

I told Louie I'd have to be convinced. He took the bird out of its cage and again it struck me how big it was. More than three feet from beak to tail and those eyes looked twice as large and sinister. It never stopped looking at me and muttering: "loser" under its breath.

Louie put him on his stand, which was actually an old wooden crucifix, gave him another saltine slathered in peanut butter and then said to him: "You're on the clock, Bones…"

The bird seemed to understand, because suddenly it was standing at attention on the top of the cross, scanning the dark horizon in all directions. He could turn his head almost 360-degrees and made a chirping sound reminiscent of an old-fashioned radar ping when doing so. This time, it took him two and a half revolutions before he stopped in mid twirl and squawked: "Big one out there. Might be a big one…"

We both looked out on the ocean, but it was dark as hell by now and the wind and the spray were kicking up. We couldn't see anything but whitecaps.

But Louie checked with the Mac and sure enough, it showed a large blip about 1,000 yards off starboard, heading north. We weren't in danger of a collision, but the big ship would come within a half mile of us.

"When it's as big as your thumb, it's a supertanker," Louie said, putting his thumb on the computer's blue readout screen. Feeding the bird another saltine, he patted its head and told him he was a good parrot.

Of course, my first thought was, well, it *is* a supertanker and even if it was a half mile away, we would have seen it eventually. But it was like Bones read my mind, because he started rotating again and after a few more turns, he said: "Loser in a small boat over there. Another loser. Over there…"

Sure enough, we saw a pair of running lights come out of nowhere, followed by the noise of an engine chugging loudly. It was a fishing boat, all nets and harpoons and radio antennas. It went by about 500 yards off our port side, blowing its horn in greeting. Louie blasted ours in return.

"The brethren of the sea," he yelled over to me as the fishing boat disappeared back into the night. "We're all out here together. No one else understands…"

It went on like that all night. Drinking beer, smoking weed and watching Bones do his thing, spotting boats near and far and always being on the money. I voiced my amazement to Louie several times, but he just waved me off and said: "He'll do anything for peanut butter. And there's a ton of it below..."

The bird's accuracy *was* spooky, and right out of one of Louie's Pirates of the Caribbean stories. But I started thinking, OK, he's brilliant, but we have radar, sonar, all that stuff and a fucking computer is sailing this thing. How does the bird really help us?

I asked Louie this as diplomatically as possible, and luckily, he'd reached a perfect storm of alcoholic euphoria and love for his parrot and decided to come clean with me.

I remember he started by saying: "Because we're on a secret mission."

What followed was typical Crazy Louie. We were definitely sailing the boat to St. Croix in the American Virgin Islands. He swore that much was on the level. But stored below, in amongst all that peanut butter he said, was an old sea chest containing something worth a "crapload of money."

"We're supposed to get to a certain coordinate off St Croix," he said. "Go in no como, meet someone doing the same thing and then trade them our lifeboat for theirs."

Trading lifeboat for lifeboat? What the hell was that?

Louie explained the two-lifeboat idea came from one of the pirate books he'd read. Sometimes instead of fighting each other, the captains of rival pirate ships would make deals for the necessities of sailing on the high seas: food for water, medicine for gold. They'd maneuver close enough to each other to exchange connecting lines, but to keep everyone honest, they'd make the actual exchange via lifeboats. You take our lifeboat filled with larder and we'll take yours.

That was why, Louie said, whenever you see a painting of a pirate ship, you'll know its accurate if it shows all different kinds of lifeboats hanging off its sides.

So that was the plan. Get the sea chest to the right coordinate at the right time. Put it in the yacht's main lifeboat. Make the switch, then go our separate ways.

But the "no como" part was important. Louie explained that meant as soon as we were nearing the rendezvous point, we'd have to shut everything down. There could be no electronics trail, no lights, no radios. No witnesses. Nothing that could put us in that spot at that time.

I started to think I knew what he was talking about. "So, when the time comes, the parrot will tell us where to go and what's around us? See and sense things we can't?"

I remember Louie looking at me, maybe a bit paler than usual.

"Well, there's that," he replied. "But—pirate captains mostly had parrots around because they thought they brought good luck in dangerous situations. So, when I was told these people we are meeting aren't exactly Boy Scouts, I figured when the time comes, we might need him for nothing more than a shit load of good luck."

I remember that's when I thought for the first time, no wonder we were being paid so much money.

We knew we couldn't stay up day and night just getting high and drinking beer, so Louie wrote out a schedule. Six hours alone on the bridge, six hours sleep time, 12 hours on the bridge together. It worked because it was easy and for the first four days, smooth sailing, thanks to the weather and our Mac computer.

But everything changed the fifth day. I remember the sky that morning was bright red. That brought back an old saying: "Red skies at night, sailor's delight. Red skies in the morning, sailors take warning."

It was soon clear a major storm system was building directly south of us. It stretched horizon to horizon and had a mix of dark and white clouds, with lightning bolts flashing all over it. Louie checked our weather radio station. They were identifying it as a localized event and that vessels in the area should simply use caution when traveling through what they considered a small, if pesky rain squall.

But it wasn't. We watched all that morning as this thing built into a motherfucker of a storm and by noon it was covering most of the sky, with the red clouds being all around us. It was like sailing into hell.

Right around this time, I remember Louie being hunched over our location indicator and remarking, maybe this was what happens to ships caught in the Bermuda Triangle. It was such a fucked-up thing to say, I got up and looked at the location indicator, too. Louie had cut out a transparent slide in the shape of what people considered the dimensions of the Bermuda Triangle and laid it over the video screen. It showed we were right in the middle of the damn thing.

The wind arrived soon after that and then the rain and then the waves. Louie had the weather station turned up full blast, but we could hear nothing about this enormous frontal disturbance we'd found ourselves in.

I was beginning to really hate sailing by now, but I knew all we could do was ride it out. We were too far from the East Coast to make a run for cover. And now that I knew there was a surprise package on board, I wasn't enthusiastic about seeing anyone until our secret mission was accomplished.

Around three that afternoon, just when the wind was at its worst, the waves their highest and the rain its most torrential, Louie went below and retrieved the parrot. He took him out of his cage and allowed him to take his place on his left shoulder.

"What do you see out there?" Louie asked it. Somehow understanding this, the bird did two near-revolutions of his head—and then took a massive crap on Louie's shoulder.

Louie was shocked, then furious. His chalk white face turned crimson. His eyes looked like they would pop out of their sockets. He dislodged the bird from his shoulder, his ruffled sleeve shirt now ruined, and roughly put it on its crucifix walking-stand. The bird started pacing up and down the cross-like structure, muttering under its breath: "This is not good. Nope. Not good, at all."

The whole thing scared the crap out of me, too. As strange as Louie was, you always had confidence in him to get you out of any tough situation. He never got flustered, never lost his cool, never gave a fuck about anything. But when I saw him crumble like that, it was the first time I thought we might be in real trouble here.

Praying the gale would blow itself out, just the opposite happened. The storm grew worse. We were tossed around like a toy boat all through that afternoon, through that night and into the next morning. It was like a nightmare that wouldn't end. I watched the waves for hours, crashing across the bow, anxious to see some indication that they were getting smaller or the sea a little less rough—but I never saw either.

At some point, I was so sick to my stomach, I had to lay out on the steering bench. Meanwhile Louie was strapped into the captain's chair, holding on for dear life with Bones nearby, squawking non-stop in between crying out: "This is not good, you losers. Nope. Not good."

That day went into another stormy night. I was viciously seasick. I was soaked, I couldn't stand up, I could hardly open my eyes. I've been down in the dumps before, but until then I thought *this* had to be the lowest point of my life. All I kept thinking was, what a way to go.

I never went to sleep the whole time; that was impossible. But I think I went semi-conscious, because at some point I forced my eyes open and saw a shooting star go right over my head. And millions of other stars we're twinkling above me. The boat had stopped rocking, and we weren't being drenched with sea spray anymore. I couldn't believe it; the tempest had finally blown over.

I sat up to see Louie, looking more ghostly than ever, but still at his post, hands melded into the steering wheel after holding it so tightly for so long. I yelled to him, but it was like he was in a trance. Perched back on his shoulder, having also ridden out the storm, was the parrot, a little ruffled but with plumage brighter than ever.

I got to my feet and stumbled over to the steering station. Louie was just coming out of it too. The bad dream was over, the storm clouds were gone, and a new day was about to begin. On cue, the entire boat was suddenly lit by a bright orange glow, a hint of the imminent sunrise. I remembered thinking: A photo of this would look perfect on a religious greeting card. It was just amazing.

"One to tell the grandkids," Louie finally spoke. "I think I have a few running around out there."

I was just so happy to be alive, I wanted to get drunk, high and anything else to blast off. Louie was right, it *was* a tale to be told.

The only one on board who wasn't happy was Old Bones Jones. He'd stayed at his post throughout the cataclysm, but he'd never stopped squawking that things were bad and that everyone involved were losers.

Even as the sun rose in indescribable beauty, the parrot was obviously under a great deal of stress. He wouldn't even eat a cracker.

Finally, Louie took him off his stand and held him in his outstretched hand. He looked the bird straight in the eye and at that moment the bird stopped moving and returned the stare.

"What's the matter, Bonesie?" Louie asked him in a very soothing manner. "C'mon, you can tell me…"

The bird's whole demeanor just dropped. I remember he was shaking his head from side to side, as if for once he was stumped for something to say.

Finally, he squawked once and said: "Old Bones Jones is old. His bones are old. Time to say goodbye…"

An instant later he exploded in a bloody mist of feathers and bone. Suddenly parrot guts were splattered everywhere.

Louie and I immediately hit the deck. We couldn't believe it. Bones had been shot, apparently by a high-powered rifle, literally blowing him to pieces.

"God damn," I heard Louie whisper. "That means we're next…"

No sooner had he said it when the bullet rounds started coming in. It was one long barrage at first, then two and three rounds at a time, indicating more than one gunman. It became non-stop.

The sizzling noise each bullet made as it went over our heads was terrifying. Like burning through thick tropical air, we could actually smell smoke coming from the damn things. That's how close they were to hitting us.

Now imagine, being out in the middle of no-fucking-where and someone is shooting at you, someone you can't see. We figured our would-be killers were in a small boat, way, *way* out there, using high-powered rifles and literally hiding behind the waves. But beyond that, we were at a loss. We couldn't even tell which direction the shots were coming from.

We crawled over to the computer and checked the surface radar. Again, it had been built to pick up big ships and super tankers, things it was crucial to avoid. But it wasn't so good at identifying smaller vessels and so it was showing nothing.

That's why the parrot had been so handy. He'd been able to sense the little stuff.

We got our own firearms out. Louie had his shiny shotgun and he'd bought me the movie-replica Thompson MG. These were awesome weapons, but they weren't much good to us now. Our stalkers were shooting at us from such a long range, they were impossible to see, never mind shoot back at.

Sails down, heads down, engines on high, we spent the next few hours watching helplessly as everything dear to us—our antennas, surface radar, running lights, navigation stuff, many of the connections to the Mac—all of it, was systematically picked off by our unseen, water-borne stalkers.

Louie said it was like plucking a Thanksgiving turkey before killing it, the poor bastard.

But *why* would someone want to kill us?

That was a very long day.

Crawling around the steering bridge, engines continuing to burn at full power, Louie was trying his best to zig-zag away from our attackers, hoping the remaining connections to the Mac would cooperate. One program that was still alive was the GPS unit—but there were times we couldn't believe what it was telling us about our position. According to the satellites, the big storm had really pushed us along and we were fast approaching the Virgin Islands and our rendezvous point. But this didn't seem real to us. Other than knowing we were pointing south we were basically sailing blind. The Mac's close-in surface radar gear had been shot to crap and our radio antennas had been the first to go.

The one good thing was, for a sailboat with its engines engaged, this thing could really move. We were hitting 25 knots sometimes. The bad thing was our persecutors had no problem keeping up with us.

Day finally turned to night again and once more Louie fooled me with his extensive knowledge of just about everything. As soon as the sun was gone and the stars came back out, he'd crawled down below and returned with a sextant.

I shouldn't have been surprised that he knew how to use the ancient-tech navigating device, but I was. "Part of my advanced anti-pirate training," he told me.

The gunfire had slackened off with the coming of darkness. Now it was a single shot every few minutes as opposed to one every few seconds. While I was still being cautious, I also started moving around the main deck a little more, constantly looking for people sneaking up and trying to board us.

It was during one of these patrols that I heard Louie literally shriek with joy.

I ran forward to find him still immersed in his sextant, an enormous smile crinkling his ghostly features.

"The GPS was right, my brother," he whispered to me, not wanting to move his instrument away from the guiding stars. "We are almost there…"

"We are almost where?" I asked. "The Caribbean?"

He finally looked over at me, still smiling, still creepy.

"We're almost at the rendezvous spot," he replied. "Maybe ninety minutes away or less."

I was shocked, and so was he, but the stars didn't lie. At that moment, another bullet flew over our heads, hit the mast, and finally killed the GPS unit. But Louie didn't even notice.

"We've got to get ready," he said instead.

He was right, we had to come up with a plan. We didn't have much left to work with. We were alone, way out here, with very little on-board power remaining, no radio, no running lights, no more GPS and a navigation device invented in the 1700s. And someone was shooting at us.

But suppose we did make it to the rendezvous point in one piece? Would our would-be trading partners turn into instant allies and protect us and the sea chest from whoever was trying to fuck with us?

Maybe…

Unless it was those same individuals who'd been trying to kill us all along. In the end, it really didn't matter. If Louie's calculations were correct, we were closer to making the coordinate than limping into some safe harbor somewhere—assuming our stalkers would even allow that to happen.

So, we went to work as best we could while still crawling around the deck, trying to stay under cover.

We dragged the sea chest up top; it was heavier than I imagined. Per Louie's suggestion, we wrapped it inside a deflated rubber life raft—a little last-minute insurance, he said. Then we put it into the yacht's port side lifeboat, making certain it was positioned dead center, so as not to capsize it once afloat.

All this took an hour, and we were beyond exhausted by this time. Hungry, thirsty, with no coffee and stressed-out from being shot at, we were a mess. But by Louie's sheer determination, about twenty minutes after that, we made it to the agreed-upon coordinate, ready to do business.

But *where* were we?

There was some land to the west, way off in the distance, that Louie said he assumed was St Croix. And judging from the dark clouds closing in from the south, another storm was heading in our direction.

But other than that, at that moment, there was nothing around us but the night and the big open sea.

I'd say we were there for about a half hour, puttering around in tight figure eights, trying to make us less of a target, before anything happened.

We got shot at a few more times. But then after what we thought sounded like fireworks way, way off in the distance, the sniping stopped. We mostly stayed down though, weapons ready, trying to listen with all we had. The wind blew up and a couple squalls went over, but that big storm was still bearing down on us and with each passing minute, we had less and less of an idea what to do.

The storm arrived around midnight. The first crack of thunder sounded so much like gunfire, we both kissed the deck and stayed there. Then it started raining…

It soon became torrential, and the waves really started to kick up. Suddenly, we hear a mechanical sound to the north of us. It was like someone screaming at first. We peeked over the side to see a Boston Whaler speedboat coming right at us, right out of the rain. It's at full throttle—and its on fire.

Now, imagine this: this boat is completely engulfed in flames yet it's going more than 40 knots. And we can see people still strapped in their seats and they're on fire, too. It was like a horror movie happening right in front of us.

Louie opened fire on it. He started screaming like a madman and blasting it with round after round from his stainless-steel friend. And that's when something hit me too—like the madness pouring out of Louie was going into my own brain, because the next thing I knew, I was shooting at the speedboat as well.

It was *very* close, but at the last moment—maybe from the gunfire or maybe a rogue wave—the Whaler turned away. It went by us in a flash and to our shock we saw it was towing a lifeboat, which was also on fire. It grazed our stern and then disappeared back into the storm.

Louie and I just looked at each other and mouthed the words: "What the fuck was that?"

A second later, another noise, coming from the same direction as the first. Suddenly a much larger vessel came out of the deluge. It was a charter fishing boat, easily fifty feet long, with two open decks. There were no sports fisherman on board, though. Instead, there were about twenty or so people dressed like pirates. *Real* pirates. Some had knives in their teeth and were wearing head bandanas. Some were waving cut-lasses—or maybe they were machetes, it was hard to tell. But the boat definitely had a skull and crossbones flag flying from its mast. And again, it was like I was caught up in a movie. None of this seemed real.

They fired at us first, but their opening barrage was way off the mark. It was tough to tell why, bad aim or the raging storm, or maybe a little of both. But one thing was familiar—the unique sizzling noise some of those bullets made as they went over us. There was no mistaking that sound. They were coming from the same weapons that had been torturing us for what seemed like days.

Another barrage followed the first but was still off the mark—so much so, they might have been considered warning shots.

But Louie wasn't into warning shots. When trouble appeared, he was usually far ahead of the curve. So as soon as the second round was fired at us, he cranked up his silver shot gun again and started returning fire directly at the charter boat, now just 100 feet away from ramming us and coming on strong.

This was not the time for buckshot. Louie was firing enormous deer slugs at it. Two at a time, they looked like barrages from a battleship. The blasts lit up the night and the rain and all of them were hitting the mark, blowing fist-sized holes in the nose of the pirate vessel.

At the same time, Louie was yelling to me to get the lifeboat ready to drop. It was only then that I realized our boat was on fire. Down near the stern, flames were burning the rigger sail, with two streams of fire racing to the top of the mast.

Maybe the inboard engines we'd been using non-stop for days finally blew up. Or maybe the flaming speedboat had more than just grazed us. Or maybe a shot from the huge pirate boat had hit something flammable. In any case, the rear quarter was on fire and the flames were spreading fast.

I ran over to the port side and prepared the lifeboat to be dropped. Louie was in the middle of a real gunfight by now, but he'd caught the pirates off guard with his no-shit, aggressive counterattack. It was so ferocious the charter boat had swerved and was no longer heading directly at us. Meanwhile, he'd switched to my Thompson and as the pirate ship went by not twenty feet away, Louie mercilessly raked its decks with machine gun fire. I could hear some people on board crying out in pain.

That's when someone fired off three flares and suddenly the battle scene became illuminated. I just remember the bullets whizzing by my ears as I unlocked the lifeboat's chain gears and started crazily spinning the release wheel, ready to bring the lifeboat down to water level.

I was screaming for Louie at the same time, telling him to get his ass over here. The fire had grown way out of control by now. The main mast, all of the main sails and everything from the mid-quarter deck on back was ablaze. We were going down, there was no doubt about that.

I remember Louie running back to the lifeboat, but by now the pirate ship had turned and was coming along our starboard side. Louie kept firing at them with the Thompson, all while I was trying to push him into the lifeboat.

That's when he turned to me and said: "All my life I've believed my purpose for being in this world was to keep you safe. That's what I'm doing now."

154

With that, he hit me so hard with the butt of the Thompson, I actually saw stars, just like in the cartoons.

I fell back into the lifeboat, cracking my head on the sea chest. Louie popped the release wheel and the lifeboat hit the water a few seconds later.

I was dazed and had blood in my eyes. I started yelling for him, but he never responded. My last sight of Louie was him back up on the steering bridge, still shooting at the pirates as the burning sailboat slowly slipped beneath the waves.

Chapter Twenty

The Swiss Life Raft

Continued From the Steve Bruce transcripts...

Al said he went unconscious shortly after that, barely aware that there was fire, smoke and a huge storm swirling around him.

He told me that while he was out, he had a disturbing dream about Crazy Louie and Old Bones Jones being in the lifeboat with him except Louie was the one squawking and the bird was talking like Socrates on meth. He said it was like an animated nightmare in 3-D.

When he finally came to, it was morning. The sea was calm. The sky was clear.

And there was nothing around him. No islands, no reefs, no other boats.

He was totally alone.

The lifeboat had been damaged at the height of the battle, and shortly after waking up Al realized the seawater was pouring into it in a dozen places. It was already too much to bail, so he simply untied the rubber raft from the sea chest, inflated it, climbed in, and let the lifeboat sink around him.

It was gone in just a few minutes.

The rubber life raft had been made in Switzerland, of all places. No surprise it had a Swiss-Army knife vibe to it. Once inflated, it was big enough and relatively comfortable. Al said one compartment was stuffed with freeze-dried food, enough to keep a dozen people fed for a while. Another compartment was stocked with bottled water. Yet another held a pullout, easy-to-assemble canopy to shade the raft's occupants from the sun. Finally, he found a store of flares and a small two-way radio.

He said he tried raising someone on the radio, but all he could hear was Spanish. He spent one night just repeating "SOS" over and over into the microphone, but never got any replies.

He also reported seeing other boats on a few occasions and frantically tried to attract their attention, even shooting off the flares. But no one ever saw him. Like being in the wrong place at the wrong time 24 hours a day. A scenario that was hardly new to him.

The hours passed into days. He was in okay shape for living on a life raft and not having to worry about catching seabirds to eat. But he said while the loneliness and isolation almost killed him, the worst was his inability to stop thinking about Louie and watching him die like he did. He said he dreamed about him almost every time he fell asleep, reliving the horror, non-stop, over and over.

His guardian angel had indeed saved him.

But now he was gone.

He said by the third day, he knew he needed to put his mind on something else—and that turned out to be opening the sea chest. It wasn't built in Switzerland, but rather Newark. It had a lock on its handle that required a key. The hinges that attached the lid to the chest were thick, worked steel featuring screw heads that had been ground down and polished. And the lid itself was sealed tight. This thing was not going to open as quick as a '61 Continental on a cold night.

Al said he knew picking the lock was not the way to go. If he broke the mechanism inside, then there would be no chance of ever getting it open. He turned his attention to the chest's hinges. They were real muthafuckers—Newark strong—and even though the Swiss boat came equipped with a screwdriver, the polished-down heads rendered it useless.

Al told me he sat there under his life raft's canopy, drinking bottled water and dining on the Swiss version of field rations, trying to think of a way to crack the chest. He knew he needed an idea that was outside the box.

Way outside...

He tried to rewind how the sea chest had made it this far. It was built in New Jersey and somehow came to be the possession of the guy who owned the sailboat. In a way, it too had been part of the lifeboat-to-lifeboat exchange even if it was just a vessel for what lay inside.

But how was the person on the receiving end expecting to open it? If the contents were sensitive in any way, then a key would be needed. But where was it? Had the two sides communicated about this before the ill-fated exchange was to be made? Or might it have been an afterthought for both sides?

Al said he wasn't sure if he just sunk into a daze or whether he actually went to sleep, but somewhere along the way, lost and drifting as he was, he had another dream. It was not about Louie this time, but about the parrot, Old Bones Jones. He said when the parrot spoke, he sounded exactly like Al's mother. And she was saying to him over and over again, "The key's under the mat."

As a kid Al sometimes had to let himself into his house after school. His mother would always tell him, if she'd run out for smokes or coffee or something, "I'll be right back, the key's under the mat."

It was a dopey, unlikely, but in the end a very lucky flash of intuition, because suddenly awake, Al reached up under the bottom of the sea chest and sure enough, there was a small brown envelope taped near one of the legs. It contained the key to the lock.

He said the lock had gotten a little fucked up during the battle, plus it was rusty, so it took some jiggling just to get the key in. Then came another ten minutes of trying to get it to turn all the way. He was only half-successful there. But he was able to open the lock just enough to get his fingers up under the lid and then pry it apart a bit with his mini screwdriver. This created only a small opening, but it was big enough for him to look inside, to see what secrets the sea chest was hiding.

Al said he always suspected the chest contained documents—stolen patents or classified information or industrial espionage. He didn't know why, but bundles of money would have seemed too tame.

As it turned out, it was holding neither money, nor scads of invaluable documents.

It was much, much better than that.

Using his trusty screwdriver and lots of motivation, by the end of the day, Al was finally able to pry the lid away from the rest of the box. The contents instantly spilled out all over his lap and legs, covering the bottom of the life raft.

Gold coins.

Lots of them.

Chapter Twenty-One

Meeting Jumbo Zal

Continued From the Steve Bruce transcripts...

But there was a complication.

Al learned this two days later, after he washed up on Saba Island, near Pigeon Cove.

He was found about an hour before sunset by an islander named Jumbo Zal. As his name implied, he was a big guy, and looked a lot like Boomer back at the Rowley Flea Market.

Zal ran a scuba shop in the Cove. He did a fair amount of business, as some of the world's best diving spots were close by. But like Al, he was always interested in making just a little bit more.

They became instant friends. Al told him everything that had happened and then showed him the chest full of coins. It turned out Zal was also an expert in numismatics. He brought Al to the scuba shop, let him shower and lent him some clothes, all XXXXL.

Meanwhile, he examined the box of coins and delivered the news to a cleaned-up Al by the light of an old kerosene lamp.

"You have two thousand and sixteen coins in here," Zal told him in Dutch-tinged English. "Two thousand of them are U.S. quarters someone spray-painted gold."

Al stopped him there. "Quarters? Painted gold? Why?"

"I have my theories," Zal replied. "But here's the good news: Sixteen coins are authentic gold doubloons in mint condition. They're worth about four thousand dollars each. That's almost sixty-five grand…"

Amazingly, Al's weird brand of luck had come through for him once again. He was a castaway, but one with more than $65,000 in his pocket. That was fifteen thousand more than he'd been expecting from the sailboat gig.

But still, something was wrong here. The bathroom fixtures on "The Last Chance" had cost more than $65,000. Why would its owner go through this ritual of exchanging lifeboats in the middle of the night for what had to be chump change for him? And again, who the fuck paints two thousand quarters gold?

"Someone in some kind of deal was getting screwed," Zal explained. "You put the good coke on top of a pile of baby powder. You put the real gold coins on top of a pile of fake ones. It all looks the same to the uneducated, at least until someone really pays attention, and inevitably someone will. And I know it ended badly for your buddy, Louie, but you're actually the lucky one, my friend. When the person on the wrong end of getting screwed found out they in fact *did* get screwed, who do you think they would have come looking for?"

Al said that piece of reality hit him like a brick. He suddenly didn't feel any sympathy for the sailboat's owner as he was obviously the one doing the screwing in this case.

And Jumbo Zal was right; he and Louie would have been targets number one for anyone seeking revenge.

They stayed up all night, drinking rum and trying to come up with a plan for Al's strange new fortune.

He didn't want to go back to the U.S., because all that money would do him no good in jail. But neither did he want to just blow it all down here in sub-tropical heaven. Laundering the valuable coins might look suspicious and what the fuck was he going to do with two thousand quarters painted gold?

Al told me later he came up with the idea just as the long night of drinking was coming to an end. It was a simple plan. Take a few handfuls of the gold quarters and sprinkle them all over the sands of Pigeon Cove, which we must remember, was the only beach—sandy or otherwise—on the island. Step two, float a story in the local media about "Fidel Castro's Missing Yacht" and the just as mysterious gold quarters it was carrying. Just why the quarters were gold, no one knew, but Castro getting swindled out of a fortune was hinted at with someone mixing in real valuable gold doubloons with the less than valuable gold-painted ones. Step three: buy a bunch of cheap metal detectors and rent them by the hour with promises of many mystery coins to be found, and maybe some real doubloons, too.

Zal loved the idea, but Al had to be up front with him. The cops were probably after him for a number of reasons by now and hooking up in any business scheme with him might be risky.

But the big guy just waved away his concerns.

"The cops are after about half the people in the Caribbean these days," he said. "It's going to take them a while before they get to you."

So, Al & Zal's was born.

They rented out the metal detectors for $30 an hour. Their first week open, several dozen people took the plunge and some found some of the mysterious gold quarters. But it was the frequency of finding them that Zal and Al were looking for. They would learn that on average people would discover one or two gold quarters in any given hour, which Zal and Al would immediately buy back from them at five dollars apiece. While maybe not quite figuring it out, these people were essentially renting the detector for twenty dollars an hour instead of thirty. Those that didn't find anything paid full price.

But then came the second part of their one-two punch business plan. At the beginning of week two, Zal arranged for a well-known off-island diving buddy of his named Pete Pistol to travel to the island and dive at Pigeon Cove. Pistol was a celebrity in the world of Caribbean diving, so his visit attracted a lot of attention from fans of that sport.

After his dive off Saba, as a "gag," Pete Pistol rented a metal detector—and in full view of lots of witnesses, tourists and media, found one of the real doubloons. With great excitement and much ceremony, Zal immediately bought it from him for four thousand dollars. The story blew up in the diving world; if you're looking for real buried treasure, try Pigeon Cove on Saba Island. There are valuable coins everywhere and they pay you for them right on the spot.

It was perfect—a scam, yes, as Pistol had been told where to look. But just to make it a little easier on their souls, as Zal would say, they agreed to drop one of the real doubloons on the beach every week. If it was found, then Al & Zal would immediately buy it back for four thousand dollars. After one week, if no one found it, they'd move its location.

After just a few weeks, the business really started rolling. In just two months, their profits had surpassed the worth of the original $65,000 of gold doubloons. This explained the high-end Porsches in the parking lot of Al & Zal's. They were both making a very nice paycheck and the business was tolerated by the island's residents and the police, because in many ways everyone knew it was a goof, but a goof that sometimes paid off.

The only issue that needed constant attention was that many of the gold quarters that weren't found on any given day had a tendency to go out with the tide. So, Al made his early morning swim every other day and retrieved them. That's what he was doing that morning the Dutch Navy divers spotted him.

I remember just shaking my head over and over as Al told me this incredible story. But at the end of it I looked at the crowded beach, the many metal detectors glinting in the rising sun. People having fun, people getting drunk. The peal of someone who'd just found a gold quarter—or worse. It seemed like the paradise Al had always tried to reach—and now after many attempts, he'd found it. He was here. An ape in essence. With some real money in his pockets for a change. It was hard to believe it could get any better for him than this.

So, the big question was why? Why turn yourself in now?

"Simple," he told me. "I miss Sue…"

Chapter Twenty-Two

A Return with a Burn

Reporters: Is it fair to say that Al's arrival home was not what you or he expected?

Steve Bruce: That's not an understatement. A reporter from your paper described it as Beatle-esque and I can't dispute that either. Once the Boston media got ahold of the story, and someone came up with the headline: "Local Conman Arrested in Paradise—Turns Himself in for Love…" nothing was ever the same again.

The crowd of new Al admirers that showed up at Logan Airport was more than a couple thousand, enough to cause State Police to seal off the Delta terminal, resulting in a bunch of flights being re-routed, delayed or cancelled. There were dozens of media-types on hand too, including reporters from Germany and Japan. The impromptu press conference in the Delta terminal lasted an hour and Al bantered with the press like a pro.

All that came to a very dramatic ending, when detectives from both Boston and Everett arrived and placed Al under arrest. The initial charge was unlawful flight. He was immediately transported to the municipal courthouse down at the Seaport to be arraigned, with a large press contingent following behind. Playing to the media, the judge ordered Al held on $5 million bond, a startling number that even the old-time bailiffs gasped on hearing it. The reason: he was a significant flight risk.

I remember thinking it would take a lot of fund raisers at Kelsey to meet that goal.

With no way of making bail, Al was going back to Bedford Junction to be held until he was transferred to a real prison.

Reporters: Even though this had been turned into a love story by the media, Al's estranged wife, Sue, was not at the airport nor the courthouse.

Steve Bruce: That's correct. It was easier to get Al home from the Islands than to get Sue to travel just a few miles to Logan Airport. She didn't want to be part of the circus. She'd turned down a number of interviews already and just stayed out of the public eye. So, I can't imagine how she felt when she heard Al was alive but going back to jail.

Reporters: Tell us what happened after Al was ordered back to Bedford Junction.

Steve Bruce: I just remember a lot of chaos bringing him downstairs to the courthouse's transportation dock. So many people, including the media, had expected him to get released on his own recognizance or at worst, a small bail, they'd been piled up at the front door waiting for him to come out. Now, suddenly everyone was trying to get to the basement to catch a picture of him boarding the bus to jail.

The bailiffs let me go with him and I had asked my wife to pick me up at the BJ. So, the bus is empty; it's just us and the driver. We drove out of the courthouse garage's back door and took a right to avoid the crowd. That was the first time we realized Harrington Square was lit up like daytime, even though it was the middle of the night. Huge klieg lights were lining the street and hundreds of people were moving about.

I wasn't aware of what was happening until that very moment because I'd been down in the Islands and somewhat out of touch. But the complication wasn't caused by the media this time—it was Hollywood.

Apparently, a TV producer had been in Kelsey's a couple weeks before and fell in love with the place, the dump that it was. He was thinking he'd make a kind of show like Cheers, just grittier. "Frowns" I think it was called. Anyway, they decided they'd shoot the pilot episode at Kelsey's instead of on a set, and that's what was happening. Literally lights, camera, action. The street's blocked off, there's lots of extras involved, lots of cops doing details, lots of Teamsters hanging around doing nothing. It was all in front us. We had to wait for them to film something on the sidewalk right outside the bar.

Al didn't say a word, at first. I remember wondering if he was in shock or something. But then, suddenly, he became very focused on what was going on outside Kelsey's.

He sat straight up in his seat and said: "Something's not right here…"

He didn't say "Hey, are they filming a movie, here?" Or "Hey, is Kelsey's on TV?" He said very distinctly: "Something's not right here..."

No sooner were the words out of his mouth when there was a terrific explosion. In my memory I thought it came from inside Kelsey's, but Al knew better. A seriously overworked transformer on an electrical pole next to the old bar had blown up, filling the square with a cloud of sparks.

Several things happened next. Kelsey's was suddenly lit up by the great flash followed by a mini-fire storm tearing through its kitchen. Luckily, it was empty due to the late hour and the filming.

Not so the building next door...

It was the St. Don Bosco Home for Little Wanderers—and it was as elderly as the saint himself. All old wood with ancient fake-brick vinyl siding, the corner of its third floor was less than a foot away from the exploding transformer. When the flames erupted, the top floor of the orphanage caught fire and it began to spread very quickly. I know. I was there. And I'd responded to many fire calls when I was on the job. But I'd never seen a fire move this fast.

By procedure Al had to leave the courthouse in cuffs, but I took them off once we got on the bus. The BJ was about thirty minutes away, but I'd planned to ask the driver to stop at the Nightside Diner so I could buy Al his last good meal for a while. The food at BJ was just OK—but nothing like the Nightside.

At least that was the plan. But suddenly we had come upon this mini-Towering Inferno. Al said nothing after that. He just jumped up, pushed the bus doors open, got out, somehow sprinted across dozens of electrical cables, and before anyone else could do anything, ran into the burning orphanage.

I must admit, I froze. Was he taking advantage of this sudden chaos to make an escape? Would Al actually run into a burning building full of kids—only to run out the back door to evade the law once again?

I got my answer a few seconds later when he stumbled back out of the building, carrying two tykes and herding a few more. The fire department was just arriving, so he left the kids for them—and ran back into the building.

He emerged about twenty seconds later with more kids, carrying some, urging others to run across the street. His face was blackened, his clothes were singed. The fire department had arrived by that point and one fireman grabbed Al and told him not to go back in the building again.

Strangely, Al just shook hands with the guy—and ran into the inferno one last time.

Chapter Twenty-Three

From Zero to Hero

Reporters: When did you first hear of your husband's heroics that night?

Sue Ford-Ferrari: Officer Bruce called me. He just said, turn on the TV quick and hung up. It sounded like a war was going on in the background. I could hardly hear him. But I turned on Channel 4 and there it was, Good Samaritan saves orphans from fire, and they had Al's mug shot in the corner of the screen.

I nearly fainted. I couldn't process what was happening. I thought Al was in jail by that time—I didn't want to go to the airport or appear in the courtroom, because I just knew both places would be crazy and even more so if I showed up. But I'd been keeping track of what was happening. In fact, Officer Bruce called me several times earlier that night just to update me on what was going on.

But now, this thing at the orphanage—all those kids Al rescued. And I know it was probably some of the very same kids who sold that piece of the Titanic and basically lied to him, which led to him escaping to the Islands in the first place. Those little bastards—yet here he was, saving their lives.

I went into a daze for about a half minute, then the phone rang again—this time it was Jimmy Fitz's wife, Monica Chase, the reporter who used to be at Channel 4. She and Jimmy flew in from LA when they heard Al was coming back and they were there at the airport and went as far as they could go with him in the courtroom. They've really stuck with him and supported him. So, when she called, I wasn't surprised.

She asked if she could interview me, and I said yes. By this time, the Boston TV news trucks were parked outside the house, and I was getting roses from The Today Show. It was already out of control.

So, I let Monica in, and she was very respectful in allowing me to talk about Al. What a great guy he was, and smart. Always helping other people, liked to have a good time. A good friend to have. Just about everyone who knew him would say the same thing. He lived an interesting life, and unfortunately, sometimes that resulted in him being at the wrong place at the wrong time.

***

Reporters: That interview your wife Monica did with Sue went worldwide and you were there. All the interest in Al's life and then his last brave act—did it surprise you?

Jimmy Fitz: I've got to say that nothing connected with Al Ferrari was ever surprising. You just expected the unexpected being with that guy. Growing up, it was always a thrill ride, just like hooky from school is a thrill ride. It always seemed like we were doing something where we didn't want to get caught. Or chasing someone. Or someone chasing us. One moment you were being chased by a gang of kids with chains and tire irons, the next thing you know, you're sitting down to dinner with your family, suddenly safe and warm. It was a strange existence and Al was always at the center of it somehow, someway.

Reporters: So, you stayed with Sue after your wife returned to the fire scene?

Jimmy Fitz: Yes, I did, because by that time, it was so chaotic outside her house and the cops weren't letting anyone else down the street, so I was really the only person she knew. I finally got her to drink a glass of wine and catch her breath and at the time I thought she'd finally started getting a grip on what had happened and what she could expect her life to be in the near future.

We turned on Channel 4 again just as Monica was doing her spot. It was clear that both Kelsey's and the Boy's Home were destroyed, but that the fire had gone out for the most part. You could see the firemen turning off the hydrants and rolling the hoses. Two vehicles arrived in the background. One was the Fire Safety Unit, the people who boarded up burned out buildings once the fire was out and the search and rescue had ended.

The other one was a hearse.

***

Reporters: You can see you visibly react on camera when the hearse showed up...

Monica Chase: I didn't realize it until I saw the rebroadcast. I knew that they'd called the hearse for Al, and it just hit me hard for a moment. Pretty unprofessional, really. But what happened next overshadowed it.

Reporters: That part of the video has also been seen worldwide. What do you remember about what happened next?

Monica, (smiling through tears): I just remember looking up to the third floor of the Boy's Home and seeing this fireman up there, on the roof, and at that instant I thought, he must be the oldest fireman in the

How To Dump a Body at Sea and Not Get Caught

world. He looked like my grandfather. But then he cupped his hands around his mouth and called down to me, just so causally, so controlled.

Reporters: And what were his words exactly?

Monica, (more tears, collects herself): He just said, "We found him. He's alive…"

Chapter Twenty-Four

The West Side Story

18 months later

Reporters: How do you like living in California? How is LA?

Steve Bruce: California is beautiful. But someone needs to come up with another description for LA. Constant motion. Nutty traffic. Expensive. But a place where fortunes can be made in a very short amount of time.

Reporters: A good description of Al Ferrari's life lately.

Steve Bruce, shrugging: If you're in the wrong place at the wrong time half the time, doesn't that mean you'll be in the right place at the right time the same amount of time? That's karma.

Reporters: It appears you're picking up the lingo pretty easily.

Steve Bruce: I have to. Al is moving in some big circles out here lately and as his chief of security I've got to know what they're talking about.

Reporters: What's going to be happening with Al in the near future?

Steve Bruce: He and Sue just bought a house in Malibu. Beautiful place. He's bought houses nearby for all his family members including his mother. He's making his friend Johnny O'Neil a millionaire for the third time, selling mansions on the country's west side, as he calls it.

In the past two weeks Al has also signed endorsement deals with NoSynx, the Swiss lifeboat company, and Sears Tools. He bought Pigeon Cove and all the businesses around it and renamed it Brother Louie Bay. He's started a seaweed clothing line and just donated $50,000 to a fund for extending the runway on Saba. He also bought Jimmy Fitz an incredibly reconditioned Caddy, the same style and model as the one they torched so long ago. Plus, he gave Kelsey some money to start his rebuild after the fire. The Diocese of Greater Boston also agreed to rebuild the Don Bosco orphanage. They wanted to name it after Al, but he asked them to name it after his father instead.

Reporters: He's leaving quite a trail behind him. Is he moving too fast?

Steve Bruce: I think Al is enjoying the ride and taking a lot of his friends with him.

Reporters: His childhood friends, yes. But how about these characters he says he met along the way? Boomer? Butterball? Jumbo Zal? You have to admit, it's quite a cast. Right out of central casting, almost.

Steve Bruce: I'm not getting your point.

Reporters: Well, has anyone ever really seen some of these people except Al? Or…could they be figments of his imagination? And could some of his stories be the same thing? Dreamed up to juice his book and movie?

Steve Bruce, (pausing): That's an interesting approach. That maybe this is all a con or something and not what it appears to be?

Reporters: Your words.

Steve Bruce: Want to ask Al that question tonight at the premiere?

Reporters: We requested press credentials but never heard back.

Steve Bruce: Let me take care of that. In fact, I'll pick you up myself.

***

Interview transcript for Joey Kelly, EDM Security, Los Angeles

Kelly: The traffic out here is the worst. I arrived a month after Steve started the security agency and asked me to help run it. It's been great ever since—except this fucking traffic.

So, the night of the premiere it was actually more fucked up. As one of the security officials, my job was to get there early. The premiere started at eight and I left at four. But the traffic screwed me again.

By the time I reached the Grauman's Chinese Theater, the red carpet was mobbed. I knew immediately this was big, even by Hollywood's standards. Four blocks around the theater had to be cordoned off from normal traffic. There were searchlights, fireworks, lots of flashes going off. A traffic jam of limousines slowly crawling forward.

Above it all, is a gigantic sign reading, Premiere tonight: "How To Dump a Body at Sea and Not Get Caught—The Al Ferrari Story."

I think that was the moment it finally sank in. This was really happening. Al's heroics saving the kids at the Don Bosco orphanage that night had been witnessed by the Hollywood producer filming in Kelsey's. He and Al hit it off immediately. Eighteen months later, Al's story is in the lights and judging from the crowd, a lot of people wanted to know what it was all about.

I finally reached the red carpet, and thank God there had been no disasters yet. Mixed in with hundreds of media types, was the Everett delegation, forty-six of Al's relatives, plus another thirty city residents including Franny DeMarco, his mom and his clipped-wing brother. Cousin Bobby of the Mass Registry was on hand, resplendent in his dress uniform. A lot of the guys from Johnny O'Neil's formerly owned funeral homes were there, too, including Johnny himself. They all knew me by now; they gave me a mock cheer as I walked by.

Next to them were the six goombahs who worked with Al at the fruit stand in the North End. And that guy standing next to them in the suit and great tan? I wonder who he is? Jimmy Fitz's wife was interviewing them, but she was nice enough to stop and say hello to me. I always have the same thought anytime I see her: how did *he* get *her*? One of life's many mysteries, I guess.

What happened next really summed up the whole night for me. I came upon my boss, Steve, and the Boston reporters who'd been tailing him and Al and a bunch of other people leading up to this big night. He was talking to them about an odd assortment of people nearby. This little group was so unusual I had to stop myself for a moment and ask if we had any paid entertainers mixed in the crowd, clowns and things.

But then I realized these were some of the key players in the whole Al saga. I could hear Steve saying to the reporters: "See the big guy in the Hawaiian shirt? That's Boomer from the Rowley flea market. Those guys over there? The ones dressed like old time convicts carrying the signs? That's Hedgehog and some of the 6Block guys. And what's their sign say? "Don't Free Butterball!" Nice likeness of the fat ass himself. Crying behind a set of bars? Perfect.

"And that guy with a seaweed hat on—that's Jumbo Zal."

I could see the reporters were moving around awkwardly as this was happening. It was clear they hadn't believed these characters existed—until they finally laid eyes on them.

Steve was just pulling out his phone when I joined them. He was doing a trick I'd seen him do more than once. He pretended he was speaking to someone on the phone when actually there was no one there. He was really good at it. Very convincing.

He had the following conversation with, as far as I could tell, no one else on the line.

"Yes, I made the request a couple hours ago. Two all-access passes for the hometown newspaper? Yes, they're here with me now. I just proved to them that Zal, Boomer, Hedgehog and all those guys are real.

"So…what? But it's only two passes. No? Nothing? How about the party at Elton's afterwards? No, there either? The afterparty at Willy's? Nothing? Really? Okay, thanks…"

Then I remember Steve turning to the reporters and saying: "I'm sorry, guys. But there's been a complication…"

———————

Streaming soon! "The Pigmen Trilogy" including digitally remastered versions of "First Blood—Dawn of the Pigmen," "Blood on the Sun—High Noon of the Pigmen" and "Blood and Wonder—Afternoon of *Poccus Homines*."

About the Authors

Mack Maloney has written more than fifty novels including the best-selling *Wingman* series and the *Codename Starman* murder mysteries, as well as three nonfiction books, *Mack Maloney's Haunted Universe*, *Beyond Area 51*, and *UFOs in Wartime*. Mack is also the host of the nationally syndicated radio show and podcast, *Mack Maloney's Military X-Files*.

Marc Zappulla has written for such celebrity figures as NHL Hall of Fame goaltender Gerry Cheevers and MLB strength and conditioning coach Brian McNamee. His first novel, *The Last Longshoreman*, was inspired by his father's thirty-year career on the Boston docks.

Now Available!

MACK MALONEY'S

Best-selling *Wingman* series, *Codename Starman* military mysteries and more…

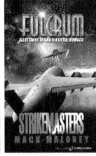

For more information
visit: www.SpeakingVolumes.us